Dealing with Mental Illness

ISSUES
(formerly Issues for the Nineties)

Volume 21

Editor

Craig Donnellan

Independence
Educational Publishers
Cambridge

First published by Independence
PO Box 295
Cambridge CB1 3XP
England

© Craig Donnellan 2000

British Library Cataloguing in Publication Data
Dealing with Mental Illness – (Issues Series)
I. Donnellan, Craig II. Series
616.8

ISBN 1 86168 141 0

Printed in Great Britain
The Burlington Press
Cambridge

Typeset by
Claire Boyd

Cover
The illustration on the front cover is by
Pumpkin House.

CONTENTS

Chapter One: What is Mental Illness?

Chapter Two: Seeking Help

Introduction

Dealing with Mental Illness is the twenty-first volume in the **Issues** series. The aim of this series is to offer up-to-date information about important issues in our world.

Dealing with Mental Illness looks at the types and causes of mental illness, how it affects different age groups and what is being done to help those who suffer from various types of mental illness.

The information comes from a wide variety of sources and includes:
Government reports and statistics
Newspaper reports and features
Magazine articles and surveys
Literature from lobby groups
and charitable organisations.

It is hoped that, as you read about the many aspects of the issues explored in this book, you will critically evaluate the information presented. It is important that you decide whether you are being presented with facts or opinions. Does the writer give a biased or an unbiased report? If an opinion is being expressed, do you agree with the writer?

Dealing with Mental Illness offers a useful starting-point for those who need convenient access to information about the many issues involved. However, it is only a starting-point. At the back of the book is a list of organisations which you may want to contact for further information.

*****

Mental health

Information from the World Health Organisation (WHO)

Mental health is a complex phenomenon which is determined by multiple social, environmental, biological and psychological factors and depends in part on the successful implementation of public health efforts to control neuropsychiatric disorders such as depression, anxiety disorders, schizophrenia, dementia and epilepsy.

Today, as many as 1500 million people worldwide are estimated to be suffering at any given time from some kind of neuropsychiatric disorder, including mental, behavioural and substance abuse disorders. A third of them may be affected by more than one neuropsychiatric ailment. Three-quarters of those affected live in developing countries.

Mental illness accounts for a significant proportion of disability due to disease and imposes a heavy burden in terms of human suffering, stigmatisation of the mentally ill and their families, and direct and indirect costs.

The major types of psychiatric and neurological disorders, generally perceived as public health problems, include:

Mood (affective) disorders

Mood (affective) disorders affect around 340 million people worldwide at any given time. They are characterised by a change in mood, which a person cannot control, to depression or elation. Such disorders typically take the form of either bipolar affective disorders or unipolar depressive disorders.
- In bipolar affective disorders, the patient goes through repeated episodes of elation and over-activity (mania) and lowered mood and decreased energy (depression).
- Mania can be accompanied by

delusions and hallucinations (disembodied voices or visions), uncontrollable excitement, incessant talking, decreased sleep, and loss of normal social inhibitions.
- Depression has the same clinical characteristics as those found in unipolar depressive disease: unaccountable sadness, diminished pleasure in daily life, weight change, disturbed sleep patterns, fatigue, feelings of worthlessness and self-blame, as well as diminished ability to concentrate and indecisiveness. Chronic depression, or dysthymia, is characterised by the persistence of such symptoms over several years.
- Depression is estimated to be present in 10% of all those seeking care at primary health care facilities worldwide.
- In the United States alone, depression costs some US$44 billion annually, which is about the same as the costs resulting from heart disease. It represents

some 30% of the total estimated annual cost of US$148 billion for all mental illness.
- The worst consequence of depression is suicide. Together with alcohol and drug abuse and psychosis, depression is implicated in at least 60% of suicides, which in 1990 accounted for 1.6% of the world's deaths.
- Depression is estimated to rank fifth in illness burden among women, and seventh among men in developing countries.

Anxiety disorders

Anxiety disorders are estimated to affect some 400 million people at any point in time. They are characterised by symptoms of anxiety and avoidance behaviour and include panic disorder, phobias, obsessive-compulsive disorder, and post-traumatic stress disorder.
- Panic disorder is marked by unpredictable episodes of intense fear or discontent, which can last for minutes or hours, and include shortness of breath, dizziness,

- palpitations, tremor, sweating, and often a fear of dying or 'going crazy'.
- Phobias are characterised by a persistent and uncontrollable fear of certain situations (for example, where physical escape would be difficult, embarrassment or humiliation possible, etc.) or of a particular stimulus (such as dogs, snakes, insects, blood, etc.).
- Obsessive-compulsive disorder is distinguished by intrusive, distressing, and senseless thoughts and by repetitive illogical behaviour to ward off misfortune, such as unnecessary and uncontrolled washing of hands.
- Post-traumatic stress disorder (PTSD) manifests itself after a catastrophic or unusual experience and persists long after the event and, in certain cases, interferes with an individual's functioning. Typical symptoms include flashbacks and dreams of the traumatic event, insomnia, numbness, detachment from other people, and an avoidance of activities and situations that can reawaken painful memories.
- PTSD is common among victims of man-made and natural disasters, military activities (for both soldiers and civilians), violence, ethnic cleansing and genocide, torture and repression, as well as among refugees.

Schizophrenia

Schizophrenia includes a group of severe psychiatric disorders that usually start in late adolescence or early adult life and often become chronic and disabling. These disorders place a heavy burden on the patient's family and relatives, both in terms of the direct and indirect costs involved and the social stigma associated with the illness, sometimes over generations. Such stigma often leads to isolation and neglect.
- There are an estimated 45 million people with schizophrenia in the world, more than 33 million of them in the developing countries.
- In acute schizophrenia the clinical signs and symptoms are more pronounced and may include delusions (false beliefs), hallucinations, jumbled and

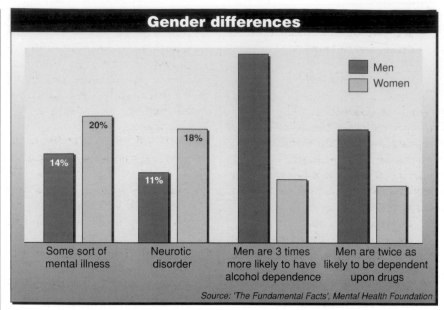

Gender differences

	Men	Women
Some sort of mental illness	14%	20%
Neurotic disorder	11%	18%
Men are 3 times more likely to have alcohol dependence		
Men are twice as likely to be dependent upon drugs		

Source: 'The Fundamental Facts', Mental Health Foundation

incoherent thoughts, a mood out of keeping with thoughts, and lack of awareness of being ill.
- Epidemiological studies in Europe and North America have shown schizophrenia to be more prevalent in low-income populations. Individuals from lower income groups, whose values, socio-economic background, education and culture are different from those of the professionals who treat them, are more readily diagnosed as schizophrenic.
- To date, research has provided little evidence for understanding the social origins of schizophrenia. But it does provide strong support for the hypothesis that social and cultural factors affect the course and prognosis of the disease.
- People affected with schizophrenia who live in developing countries seem to be more responsive to treatment than those in developed countries. A WHO follow-up study of people, diagnosed as suffering from schizophrenia in nine countries, suggested that two years after the first treated episode of the disease, 58% were reported to have recovered in Nigeria, 50% in India, and only 8% in Denmark.
- The cost of schizophrenia to society is enormous. In the United States, for example, the direct cost of treatment of schizophrenia has been estimated to be close to 0.5% of the gross national product.

Dementia

Dementia is a brain syndrome usually of a chronic or progressive nature, which is manifested by a decline of memory, comprehension, learning capacity, language and judgement, as well as of the ability to think and to calculate. This syndrome occurs in Alzheimer's disease (AD dementia), in some but not all cases of cerebrovascular disease, and in other conditions affecting the brain, such as Pick disease, Creutzfeldt-Jacob disease and Parkinson disease.
- Worldwide, around 22 million people suffer from dementia.
- Global incidence rates for dementia of all types have been estimated to be less than 1% per annum, with the risk of the age-specific AD and vascular dementia rising steeply above the age of 60 years.
- AD and vascular dementia far outnumber other cases of dementia and are the two principal kinds of dementia in the elderly (senile dementia). The senile dementias have assumed great importance in public health because more people today live into the age of high risk.
- The number of people suffering from senile dementia in Africa, Asia and Latin America may exceed 80 million in 2025.
- Because of the increasing number of road-accidents and strokes, which can cause brain damage, presenile dementia is a major problem in many countries.
- There is an association between

a past history of heavy drinking and the onset of dementia or depression in later life.

Epilepsy

Epilepsy is a neurological disorder which is characterised by totally uncontrollable fits that occur repeatedly, sometimes more than once a day. They start suddenly, are accompanied by convulsions and stop abruptly with or without loss of consciousness.

- Epilepsy is estimated to affect approximately one in every 130 people worldwide. In all, there are more than 40 million people of all ages and social conditions who are affected by epilepsy with 2 million new cases each year. 80% of those affected live in developing countries.
- People affected with epilepsy are highly stigmatised. One of the reasons is that in many countries, epilepsy is erroneously perceived as an infectious disease. The affected people and their families are shunned to the point of isolation.
- More than 80% of newly-diagnosed patients with epilepsy can be successfully treated today with anti-epilepsy drugs and lead normal lives. In many cases adequate treatment can be provided at an average cost of US$5 per patient per year. Unfortunately, half of those affected are treated improperly or not at all.
- Some infections and brain injuries are among the major causes of epilepsy. Epilepsy may be caused by genetic factors and infectious diseases in the prenatal period, by birth asphyxia and brain injury during labour, and, in the post-natal period, by febrile convulsions, infectious (e.g meningitis, encephalitis) and parasitic (e.g. malaria, schistosomiasis) diseases and brain damage caused by alcohol, trauma or toxic substances (e.g. lead, pesticides).
- Prevention of epilepsy is possible through prenatal care, safe delivery, control of fever in children, reduction of brain injury, control of infectious and parasitic diseases, and genetic counselling.

Current research provides strong evidence that mental disorders are of biopsychosocial origin.

- There is a strong interrelationship between some tropical disease and neuropsychiatric disorders and impairments. Infestations of cysticercosis (tapeworm), for example, may result in brain lesions leading to epileptic seizures.
- The quality of a person's social environment influences both his or her vulnerability to mental illness and the course of that illness. Poverty, overcrowded living conditions, job insecurity, marital problems, man-made and natural disasters, ethnic violence and violence against women, children and the aged, wars – all of these influence negatively the mental health of the world's populations.
- Demographic factors such as population ageing and urbanisation accentuate the public health and social magnitude of mental illness.
- Substance abuse – harmful use of alcohol, illicit drugs and other psychoactive substances – aggravates all other forms of mental illness and has also been proved to have a major negative impact on public health in general.

© WHO/OMS, 1998

Serious mental illness

Information for young people

How many people are affected?

Serious mental illness affects about 1-2 in every 100 people. It hardly ever occurs in children and is very rare in teenagers. Even so, teenagers often worry that they may be 'going mad' when they are feeling stressed, confused or very upset. In fact, feelings like these are only rarely a sign of mental illness. Mostly, they get a lot better if you talk to someone you trust about them.

Teenagers are often frightened to talk about their feelings in case people think they are mentally ill or 'mad'. This is because many people do not understand what mental illness is – and that it can be successfully treated. This is not helped by media stories about the rare times that a tragedy occurs or something goes badly wrong.

The two illnesses described in this article are schizophrenia and bipolar affective disorder (sometimes known as manic depression). They are the most common of the group of serious mental illnesses known as psychoses.

Schizophrenia

Schizophrenia is the commonest form of psychosis. Symptoms include delusions, thought disorder and hallucinations.

Delusions are unshakeable beliefs which are obviously untrue. For example, an ill person might strongly believe that there is a plot to harm them – that they are being spied on through the TV or being taken over by aliens.

Thought disorder is a serious disturbance in thinking clearly. It is more than just feeling a bit muddled or confused at times. Other people may find the person hard to understand because their sentences don't make sense and their ideas are all jumbled up.

Hallucinations are when someone sees, hears, smells or feels something that isn't really there. The most common hallucination that people have is hearing voices. If someone has a hallucination, it doesn't necessarily mean they are ill. In schizophrenia, hallucinations happen often and are believed to be totally real by the person having them. This can be frightening and can make them believe that they are being watched or picked on. People who are having these experiences may act strangely. For example, they may talk or laugh to themselves as if talking to somebody that you can't see. This is quite different from the talking and laughing of healthy children or adults caught up in imagining, inventing or playing.

A person with schizophrenia usually has all of these symptoms. They may also become quiet and wrapped up in their own world and lose their interests and motivation. They find it hard to concentrate and often neglect to keep themselves clean.

The symptoms of schizophrenia are sometimes mistaken for moodiness or teenage rebellion. They can also be mistaken for quite different problems, such as depression.

Bipolar disorder

Bipolar affective disorder is a condition in which the main feature is extreme changes of mood. The moods are usually way 'over the top' – considering the person's normal personality and the current situation. There are long periods of being unusually happy, 'high' or 'manic', and long periods of being unusually miserable, 'low' or 'depressed'.

When someone is manic, they can become very overactive, loud and careless. They take risks they would not normally take, and may get into serious trouble. For example, they may spend money they do not have, or get very aggressive. They can also suffer from delusions, for example, that they are famous, or have special powers.

When someone is depressed, they become very miserable, moody and withdrawn. They may have delusions, which make them believe that they are ugly, or guilty of terrible crimes. Life may seem pointless, and they may try to kill themselves.

Periods of illness can last for weeks or months. The quicker they're treated, the shorter they tend to be.

What causes psychotic illness?

This is still not fully understood. In both schizophrenia and bipolar affective disorder, there are abnormalities in the chemistry of the brain. This causes changes in thoughts, feelings and behaviour.

There are a number of factors which make a person more likely to develop a psychotic illness. Usually, a combination of these is needed to trigger the illness. Genetic factors play a part, probably by increasing the risk of an imbalance in brain chemistry. Having a parent or close relative with schizophrenia or bipolar disorder means that a person will have a slightly greater than normal chance of developing the condition.

A psychotic illness can be triggered in a person who is 'at risk' by a number of factors. These include physical illness, stressful events and mind-altering drugs such as lysergic acid diethylamide (LSD) and cannabis.

The first step towards getting help is to recognise that there may be a problem and to seek advice. The person with the illness may not notice the problem and deny that there is anything wrong. Often, other people notice that the ill person is not functioning as well as they normally do. Parents are often the first to ask for help. The family doctor or school nurse can give good advice. They will be able to get specialist help if it is needed. A psychiatrist may need to visit the person to find out whether or not they are ill, and to offer the treatment that is needed.

Getting help

The goals of treatment are:
- to reduce or stop the symptoms of the illness.
- to prevent the symptoms from recurring.
- to help restore a normal life.

Most treatment is provided by a psychiatrist on an out-patient basis. Medication usually plays an important role in the treatment of psychotic illnesses. It helps to correct the chemical imbalance in the brain. Medication usually needs to be taken for some time, so that it can reduce or stop the symptoms of the illness and prevent the person getting ill again. As with medication of any kind, there may be side-effects. The doctor who prescribes the medication should discuss the side-effects and how to avoid them. Sometimes, side-effects can't be avoided completely, and people often want to know if they can stop taking the medication, or change to a different one. It's important to ask the doctor for advice about this before deciding what to do. Stopping medication too soon can cause a person to get ill again.

Other forms of treatment are also important. Both the patient and their family will need help to understand the condition, to cope successfully and to prevent the illness recurring. Support is often needed to rebuild the confidence needed to continue with school, college or work.

If a person becomes very ill they may need in-patient care. Teenagers are usually admitted to a small specialist unit for people their age that can provide treatment, education and help for the family. The unit provides safety and round-the-clock care.

Looking to the future

Psychotic illness can have damaging effects on a person's education and future if it is left to go untreated. With treatment, the chances of a normal life are good. Even though some people do get ill more than once, they can recover. In spite of the illness, they can enjoy a full and satisfying life.

© Royal College of Psychiatrists

Victims of circumstance

Chris Johnston on new research indicating dangerous links between child psychiatric problems and class, gender and family instability

One in 10 British children had a mental disorder last year, according to the most comprehensive survey of adolescent mental health ever undertaken.

Conduct disorders (aggression or antisocial behaviour) affected 5%, while 4% had emotional disorders such as anxiety and depression and 1% were considered hyperkinetic (inattention and overactivity). More boys than girls suffered from problems – 10% of five to 10-year-olds and 13% of 11 to 15-year-olds. The figures for girls were 6% and 10%.

The research involved more than 10,000 face-to-face interviews with parents of children aged five to 15 years and 4,500 with young people aged 11 to 15, as well as a questionnaire to the children's teachers.

Prof Robert Goodman – who headed a team that involved the Office for National Statistics, the Institute of Psychiatry and Maudsley Hospital – said the one in 10 figure was extremely high. 'It's a very serious problem; you can't find physical disorders that are that common,' he said.

Although higher figures had been produced by other research, Goodman said very strict criteria had been used so only children with serious symptoms were included.

The finding needed to be taken seriously, he said, not least because these children were suffering and their lives, as well as those of their families, were being disrupted.

'But beyond that, part of the interest and importance of child mental health is that it does predict many problems in adult life. This 10% are at much greater risk of abusing drugs, having health problems, being involved in criminal activity and being long-term unemployed,' Goodman says.

One of the most striking findings of the research was the relationship between social class and mental health. Disorders were more likely among children in families where neither parent worked (20%) than those in which both were employed (8%).

The difference was almost as large when measured by gross weekly household income of less than £200 compared with £500 or more – 16% as against 6%. Similarly, 14% of children with mental disorders came from families in social class V (unskilled occupations), while the figure for those from professional families (social class I) was just 5%.

Mental disorders in children were twice as likely in lone-parent families, compared with those with two parents (16% and 8%). Similarly, incidences were much more common when the primary care giver, usually the mother, had no educational qualifications (15%) compared with those that had been to university (6%).

Twice as many children with a mental health problem had a parent with a similar problem, such as anxiety or depression (47% and 23%), and affected children were also twice as likely to come from broken families.

Goodman says the research had not tried to determine the causes of mental illness in children, and this would require a different type of study. Rather, he says, the Department of Health commissioned the study to help it design services for children with serious mental health problems. 'Inner city areas with a high number of poor single parent families in social housing need a lot more money for services, because there will be more children needing help,' he says. 'In the recent past, money has been moved away from, for instance, inner London and out into more rural areas probably more than was justified, because inner city areas have much more deprived populations.'

He hoped that the findings would lead to the government providing more funding to areas that needed better mental health services and said its commitment to tackling social exclusion suggested action would be taken. Further analysis of the findings will take place, and Goodman hopes funding will be made available to allow follow-up studies of participants.

• *Mental Health and Adolescents in Great Britain* (£35: ISBN 011 621373 6) is available from the Stationery Office (tel: 020 7242 6393).

© Guardian Newspapers Limited, 2000

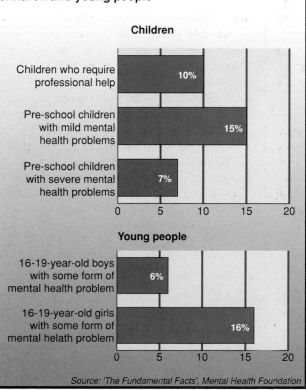

Children and young people

The prevalence of mental health problems among children and young people

Children

- Children who require professional help: 10%
- Pre-school children with mild mental health problems: 15%
- Pre-school children with severe mental health problems: 7%

Young people

- 16-19-year-old boys with some form of mental health problem: 6%
- 16-19-year-old girls with some form of mental helath problem: 16%

Source: 'The Fundamental Facts', Mental Health Foundation

Mental health – facts and figures

Mental health problems are common among young people

Incidence

Mental health problems are common among young people. It has been estimated that up to 25 per cent of children and young people under the age of 16 have a diagnosable mental health problem. These problems include depression, deliberate self-harm, eating disorders and substance misuse. The Department of Health estimates that between 10% and 20% of children will have a problem that is severe enough to require help.

Stresses

The family

Families are becoming more diverse with increasing numbers of children and young people experiencing some form of loss through divorce, separation, or bereavement. All children and young people need to feel loved, valued and respected, to have discipline and supervision, and to be with adults who build them up rather than put them down.

School problems

For some young people, difficulties at school such as bullying, peer pressure, boredom, exam stress or problems relating in school exclusion can lead to mental distress.

Bullying, which may take the form of physical abuse, name-calling and teasing, is a common form of discrimination causing great distress. Around a quarter of pupils in a survey reported they sometimes felt afraid of going to school because of bullying

School exclusion means young people are missing out on their education, making them more vulnerable to future unemployment, anti-social behaviour and crime. It also reduces opportunities for vital social contact with their peer group and makes the transition to adulthood harder.

Discrimination

Discrimination on grounds such as race, gender, sexuality and disability can cause mental distress in young people by undermining self-confidence and reducing opportunities at school, work and socially.

Poverty, social hardship and homelessness

Children and young people's mental well-being is greatly affected by poverty and social hardship. The economic, social and political context of their lives is largely beyond their control. A reasonable standard of housing and overall standard of living, together with a wider social network beyond the family, can help minimise the risk of mental health problems in young people.

Alcohol, drug and solvent misuse

For some young people, the use of alcohol, drugs or solvents may be for social reasons or as a means of escape or way of coping with difficulties. At the same time they may contribute to problems such as low self-esteem and involvement in crime. Drinking excessively can lead to feelings of insecurity, depression and aggression that may lead on to feeling isolated, lonely, subdued or hopeless.

The effects of different drugs on mental well-being vary from one individual to another and depend on the situations in which they are taken. Effects may range from feelings of tension, panic, anxiety, low concentration, confusion and depression, and sleep problems. For some drugs, stopping regular use may lead the person to feel depressed or run down for some time. Young people with a mental health problem are especially vulnerable to the effects of drugs.

Physical and sexual abuse

Child abuse can cause major mental health problems. One study found that almost half of the men and women psychiatric inpatients studied had experienced physical and/or sexual abuse. It is estimated that one in ten children suffers some form of abuse and disturbance, and without help, problems often persist into adult life causing serious personality and relationship problems and in some cases mental health problems.

Mental health problems

Depression

About 2 in 100 children under the age of 12 are depressed to the extent that they would benefit from professional help. At least 5 per cent of teenagers are seriously depressed and twice that number show significant distress. Causes of depression are varied and can be linked to family or relationship problems, pressure at school or worries about the future.

Suicide

Suicide accounts for 20 per cent of all deaths of young people aged 15-24, and is the second most common cause of death for young men after road accidents. Among young people under the age of 25 there are two suicides a day in the United Kingdom and Republic of Ireland. Attempted suicide amongst young people has been increasing during the 1990s. There are estimated to be around 19,000 suicide attempts in adolescents every year, with young women the most likely to attempt suicide.

Coping

Young people find listening to music to be the most helpful activity for addressing and preventing stress and anxiety. Most young people find discussing problems with friends or relatives to be a useful strategy for coping with and preventing anxiety. Other methods for addressing problems include exercising, keeping busy, resting, seeking advice from a GP, counsellor or social worker and consulting books and magazines. Only a small minority of young people rely on the use of drugs in order to cope with stress, and of those who do, the majority agree that this activity offers no long-term benefits.

Positive steps for young people

There are many different positive steps that young people can take for their mental health. The important thing is to find ways that work for them. There may be times when they need support from other people and they need to be encouraged to seek help and not feel they have to struggle on alone. You could suggest the following steps that work well for many young people:

Being creative

Scribble, draw, paint, make a collage or write about how you are feeling. Doing something creative is a good way of converting negative feelings into something more positive.

World Mental Health Day

World Mental Health Day (WMHD) was established by the World Federation for Mental Health and is co-sponsored by the World Health Organisation (WHO). WMHD is celebrated all over the world on the 10th October. It provides a unique opportunity for a wide variety of groups and organisations to raise awareness about mental health.

The Health Education Authority has co-ordinated the WMHD campaign in England, on behalf of the Department of Health, since 1995.

The campaign aims to raise awareness that discrimination, on the basis of age, sexuality, or race, for example, greatly increases vulnerability to mental health problems. Discriminatory attitudes and practices exclude people and also damage confidence and self-esteem, particularly of young people. The campaign provides a phoneline, regional briefing days and a wide range of resources to support local action around WMHD. The campaign works in partnership with the Health Education Board for Scotland (HEBS) and Health Promotion Wales (HPW) so that a range of campaign resources are also available in Scotland and Wales.

Letting out your emotions

It's fine to cry or let people know you are angry. Bottling up feelings only creates more problems.

Taking time for yourself

Listen to music, read a book, see a film, have a relaxing bath, give yourself time to think about things – whatever works for you.

Seeing friends

Seeing friends is good for your mental well-being. If you're feeling isolated and don't have many friends around, join a local group or activity where you can get involved and meet new people.

Getting active

Exercise is a good way of converting your anxiety and emotions into positive energy that is good for your body and mind.

Talking about it

Find someone you can talk to about your worries or concerns. It could be a friend, teacher, someone in your family or another adult you can trust.

Finding space for yourself

It may help to find your own 'safe place' where you can think through any problems. You can use it as a place to retreat to when you want time for yourself.

• The above information is an extract from the Government's Wired for Health web site which can be found on www.wiredforhealth.gov.uk

© Wired for Health

Women and mental illness

What is mental illness?

The term mental illness is a psychiatric definition and based on a medical model of health and illness – many people prefer to use the term emotional or mental distress to describe what they are experiencing.

Generally speaking mental illnesses can be divided into two types:

• Neurotic – characterised by behaviour that although perhaps strange, is still considered to be in touch with reality.
• Psychotic – characterised by behaviour that is considered out of touch with reality such as aural or visual hallucinations or extreme mood swings.

At one time the medical professions were happy simply to differentiate between 'neurotics' and 'psychotics' – this situation has now changed and there are many different labels for mental illnesses but it is important to remember that they are categories and sometimes people don't fit into them very well – a lot of people who have been diagnosed don't find the diagnosis useful and, on the other hand, others are relieved to be diagnosed.

Most forms of diagnosed mental illnesses come under the neurosis category – you can see from the list below that these are easier for other people to identify with from their own life experience.

Neurotic

Anxiety/Phobias
Depression (including acute)
Post Natal Depression

Eating Distress
Post Traumatic Stress Disorder
Obsessive Compulsive Disorder

Psychotic
Schizophrenia (including hearing voices and paranoia)
Manic depression/Bi-Polar Disorder
Hypermania

Mental illnesses that do not fall within these categories include:
- Borderline Personality Disorder
- Dementia
- Substance Abuse – this is sometimes categorised as a mental illness.

Possible causes of mental distress

There are several reasons why women may find themselves experiencing mental ill health – these can be loosely divided into social or environmental reasons and biological reasons.

Social/environmental
A difficult, deprived or abusive family background:
As a child you may not have received enough love or sense of security to shore you up in adulthood, or you may have experienced actual deprivation, abuse or neglect.

Stressful life events:
Even the most well-balanced person with a good support system can find it difficult to cope with life experiences such as poverty, racism, bereavement or being a victim of crime. Women's lives can be extremely stressful – they may be working in the home as a parent, partner and/or carer and often outside the home too in part-time or full-time jobs. The effects of this double burden are often taken for granted.

Suppression of feelings:
You may have learnt from an early age that it's not right to express feelings, or that you must be seen to be coping and feelings are things to be swept under the carpet.

Biological
Bio-chemistry:
Your actual physical make-up may be what determines the extent to which you are able to manage.

Genes:
The likelihood that you will experience mental distress is inherited, i.e. it is in your DNA/genetic make-up and is unalterable.

In order to understand mental distress we need to look at how the above categories interact.

For example, it is now known that when you express your feelings your bio-chemistry changes – scientists have analysed the tears cried when someone is peeling an onion and the tears cried when someone is upset; the tears cried when upset contain a stress hormone that is not present in tears from peeling an onion, so when you are crying about something that upsets you, you are actually eliminating the stress hormone from your body and therefore doing yourself a lot of good.

Another example that highlights the difficulties in defining mental illness as either social or biological is what happens when we experience anxiety. When we get anxious our body increases the amount of adrenalin produced. This triggers off lots of emergency responses in our body (often called the 'fight or flight' syndrome) – if you have to contain these responses (i.e. you learn that you should not express these feelings) your anxiety level will increase.

So we could classify anxiety as mental distress that is learnt. However, it may be that some people produce more adrenaline than others in which case we are looking at a biological origin for anxiety.

What we do now know is that when we express our feelings our bio-chemistry changes.

Treatments for mental distress

There are three major categories of treatments:
- Minor tranquillisers
- Anti-depressants
- Major tranquillisers (also known as anti-psychotics)

Minor tranquillisers
These are generally given to people who are experiencing anxiety or who are unable to sleep. They were prescribed extensively in the 60s and 70s particularly to women. In the 80s the medical profession realised that people were becoming dependent on these drugs.

Minor tranquillisers stop working after the first three to four months.

Anti-depressants
These are the most popular drugs: people who use them rate them more highly than people using other drugs. You need to take them for 10 to 14 days before they have an effect. You will experience the side-effects first so if you take them you will feel worse before you feel better.

Major tranquillisers

These are principally prescribed to people who have been diagnosed as schizophrenic. They have a sedative effect, i.e. they slow you down, and generally things take on less importance.

The side-effects of major tranquillisers can be horrendous. A woman who had taken major tranquillisers asked afterwards: 'Would you take a drug that stops you from being able to shit, think and have sex?' Other side-effects are uncontrollable shaking, dribbling and restlessness. They are informally called the 'liquid cosh'. A side-effect of long-term use is tardive dyskinesia which is a disorder of the central nervous system – this is also called the largactil shuffle which is what makes people on psychiatric units look 'mad'.

Talking treatments

These are patchily available and are unlikely to be offered to someone diagnosed as having a severe mental illness. Many GP practices now employ on-site counsellors. Exploring your distress with a counsellor or therapist may help you to understand the origins of your distress, experience the feelings that lie beneath it and obtain support in what may feel like a very isolated position.

Behaviour therapy

Again this is patchily available. It is a programme that helps people to change their behaviour bit by bit. A good example is someone who is afraid of lifts: firstly they will go into a lift and keep the doors open, then they will progress to going in and closing the doors, and hopefully they will be able to move on to going up a floor until they feel confident to use a lift unaccompanied.

This therapy works well for some people but as it doesn't address the underlying anxiety it does not work for others.

Alternatives

Complementary therapies are becoming more widely available and are increasingly recognised as a beneficial treatment for people with mental ill health. There are also some crisis centres available as an alternative to hospitalisation. (Please see our factsheet on Complementary Therapies for further information.)

• The above information is from Threshold Women and Mental Health Initiative. See page 41 for their address details.

© Threshold Women and Mental Health Initiative

The extent of mental health problems

How many people experience mental health problems?

Estimates for the prevalence of mental health problems in the population vary considerably, and should be treated with caution. Different studies use different denominators and measures that are not necessarily comparable.

For example, some calculations are based upon a point prevalence, i.e. mental health problems at any point in time; others use lifetime prevalence, i.e. the likelihood of a person developing mental health problems in a lifetime; and others use rates per year. Furthermore, some figures relate to a percentage of the whole population, or within the adult population only; some may be based on figures for England and Wales, and others for the UK as a whole. Definitions as to what constitutes a mental health problem may also differ.

Some examples of prevalence rates are given below:
• Research suggests that 1 person in 4 will experience some kind of mental health problem in the course of a year.
• 10-25% of the general population annually present with mental health problems, usually in the primary care setting. Within this figure, 2-4% will have a severe mental illness, a smaller number within this group will have a severe and enduring mental illness.
• Estimates for the number of people with severe and enduring

mental health problems vary from 0.3-1.5% of the adult population.

What are the main types of mental health problems?

Mental health problems have been defined and classified to enable professionals to refer people for appropriate treatment and care. However, there is an ongoing debate about the usefulness of certain diagnostic categories such as schizophrenia. Therefore the use of diagnoses should be treated with caution, and should not be seen as an indicator of the severity of mental ill-health. For example, if a person is given a diagnosis of psychosis, it does not necessarily mean that they are unable to fulfil their own potential and to lead a full life.

Neuroses

• In a survey covering Great Britain, 1 in 6 adults had experienced some form of 'neurotic health problem' in the previous week. The most common 'neurotic disorders' were anxiety and depressive disorders.

Anxiety

Anxiety is characterised by excessive worrying and agitation accompanied by physical symptoms such as rapid breathing and a fast heartbeat. It can become a problem if the response becomes exaggerated and interferes with daily living.

- More than 1 in 10 people are likely to have a 'disabling anxiety disorder' at some stage in their life.
- An estimated 13% of the adult population will develop a specific form of anxiety known as a phobia at some point in their life. This is characterised by a specific fear of an object or situation that can adversely affect a person's life.
- Another form of anxiety known as obsessive compulsive disorder (OCD) is where the person experiences obsessive thoughts associated with some form of compulsive behaviour. Although it is rare amongst people requesting help from services, large-scale epidemiological studies have suggested that around 2.5% of people are likely to experience OCD at some point in their life.

Depression

The term 'depression' is used to describe a range of moods, ranging from low spirits to more severe problems where depression interferes with everyday life. Symptoms may include a loss of interest and pleasure, excessive feelings of worthlessness and guilt, morbid and suicidal thoughts and weight loss.

- An estimated 1 in 10 people will have some form of depression at any one time.
- Estimates for the lifetime prevalence of depression vary, ranging from 1 in 6 to 1 in 4. It can occur at any age, but is most common in people aged 25-44 years.
- An estimated 1 in 20 people will have serious or 'clinical depression' at any one time. By the year 2020, it has been estimated that clinical depression will be second only to chronic heart disease as an international health burden; this is measured by its cause of death, disability, incapacity to work and the medical resources it uses. More severe episodes of depression last between 3 and 9 months, although there is a high risk of recurrence.

Psychosis

The term 'psychosis' is used when a person's ability to distinguish between reality and imagination is affected, such as in manic depression and schizophrenia.

- A survey covering Great Britain suggested that 4 per 1,000 of the adult population will experience some form of psychosis in the course of a year.

Manic depression

Manic depression is associated with severe and frequently recurrent depression, and usually involves extreme mood swings, from depression to elation and over-activity (mania). It is sometimes referred to as bi-polar mood disorder to reflect the two mood states.

- Approximately 1 in 100 adults in the UK will experience manic depression at some point in their life.
- In the UK, there are 370 hospital admissions per 10,000 of the population per year for manic depression; only 3% of these are first-time admissions. This reflects the recurrent nature of manic depression.
- An estimated 20% of people who have a first episode of manic depression do not get another.

Schizophrenia

Schizophrenia can be characterised by two groups of symptoms: abnormal experiences such as feeling out of control, hallucinations and delusions, and symptoms which represent a loss in functioning such as sleep problems, a lack of energy and low motivation.

- An estimated 1% of the population will have schizophrenia at some point in their life.
- Other estimates suggest that between 3-4 per 1,000 of the population have schizophrenia at any one time.
- After a first episode, it is expected that approximately a quarter of people with schizophrenia will make a good recovery with some form of treatment within 5 years, two-thirds will experience multiple episodes with some degree of disability between them, and 10-15% will develop severe long-term disabilities.

- The above is an extract from *The Fundamental Facts* which is produced by the Mental Health Foundation. See page 41 for address details.

Phobias

Written by David J. Hill BSc Hons (Psychol)

Before going into the area of phobias, let's have a look at the emotions which form their roots. These are fear and anxiety. The word 'fear' stems from the old English 'faer', meaning sudden calamity or danger. 'Anxious' comes from the Latin 'anxius' meaning troubled in mind about some uncertain event. Perhaps it is apt that the word is related to a Greek root, meaning 'to press tight or to strangle'.

There is a difference between anxiety and fear. Fear is immediate, it happens in the present whereas anxiety is effectively concern about some future event.

How does fear work?

Fear causes changes in the body. When we are frightened, our heart rate accelerates, our pupils dilate, we become pale, our blood pressure rises, our throat dries and we may tremble. These are manifestations of our body's gearing itself up for action. The heart rate increases to pump more blood through the system, readying the muscles for use. Our pupils open to let in more light, improving our ability to perceive movement. Blood is diverted away from the digestive system and the skin for use in the muscles and brain, hence the pallor and dry throat.

The net result of these changes is that our body is ready for instant action, ready to fight a foe or run away from it. This is the classic 'fight or flight' reaction common to all mammals.

Does fear help?

Think for a moment what life would be like without fear. To those with phobia and/or anxiety problems this may seem like the height of luxury. However, life without fear would be immensely dangerous. Supposing, for example, you encountered a vicious animal. Without fear, you might be tempted to make the animal's acquaintance. Now, it's said that animals can sense fear but I wouldn't recommend hanging around to see if animals can sense lack of fear. The animal's instinct would be to see you as lunch; it would probably be quite grateful if you stood still rather than running or fighting when it started to attack.

The same principle can be applied to any situation where fear is a factor. Our instinctive caution has stood us in good stead when it comes to surviving as a race.

Fear also helps us in other ways. Every performer admits to stage fright. Without the sharpening of the senses caused by this fear, the performances would be pretty lacklustre. Similarly, if there were no fear, no one would bother with roller coasters, horror movies, motor racing, snowboarding or bungee jumping. In these circumstances, fear is actively sought as a stimulus to enrich life.

So, why do fear and anxiety cause problems?

The feelings experienced by phobics and those with chronic anxiety are no different from the fears of ordinary people. The mechanisms and events are the same but the circumstances are very different. People who have these problems are usually quite normal in themselves. It is their susceptibility to the stimuli of fear and anxiety that are abnormal.

Unsurprisingly, ordinary people find this hard to understand. Their phobic counterparts seem to behave oddly, being unusually timid, or inexplicably terrified of apparently harmless things. The most effective way to explain your feelings to your peers is to ask them to visualise the most frightening thing they have ever experienced. Can they remember how they felt then? Telling them that you can feel the same without the benefit of a rational cause can put the matter in the realm of their own experience, giving them an insight into the way you feel.

Fear or phobia?

Very few people, if any, are not frightened of anything. Their human fears may be apparent or might be suppressed but there will always be something which at least causes disquiet in an individual. Most people, though, manage their fears and are not unduly disturbed by them. Phobics, on the other hand, cannot do this. Their phobia, no matter what the cause, is beyond their capacity for management.

In general, people with phobias are often in a state of constant anxiety. They fear what they feel is liable to happen to them. For example, many arachnophobics not only fear spiders, they also fear the possibility of a spider's presence, whether that is likely or not. In some cases, their fear is such that anything which is even remotely spider-like or suggestive of a spider is the cause of a violent fear reaction. The same applies to many specific phobias, where the fear is of an object, organic or otherwise. The main point is that the level of fear is unduly high, and is abnormally easily triggered.

Fear x fear

Nobody likes to be thought of as lacking in any respect in modern society. In the case of many phobias, especially the complex ones like agoraphobia and social phobia, the sufferer fears the opinions of others as much as the phobic situation. One who fears being seen as a fool in a situation which he or she knows is of no consequence to others is under pressure on two counts. The individual becomes frightened of becoming frightened and, not surprisingly, feels the weight of this twofold stress.

Coping strategies

Human beings are nothing if not adaptable and will evolve coping strategies. But some coping strategies are better than others. As a simple analogy, let's imagine you burn yourself on a hot iron. Common sense dictates that you would not put your hand on the iron again, at least not without first checking it is cool. The phobic reaction in this instance would be to never again go near an iron, avoid things which are remotely like irons and, naturally, never get the ironing done.

Problems occur when the strategies deny activities seen as normal. To avoid irons is irrational, as is avoiding going out, social functions, driving, situations where there might be spiders or snakes, heights, enclosed spaces and all the other phobia triggers.

These are examples of mal-adaptive coping, where the individual loses out in some way. Other examples of such strategies are common. Some turn to drink, some start to smoke too much, some abuse drugs – prescription or otherwise – and some do all three. None are of any real benefit and are certainly no solution.

What about treatment?

Often, phobic and anxious people find themselves in a dreadful limbo, not knowing where to turn in their misery. Phobias can create all manner of upsetting feelings and symptoms, not one of which is pleasant. These can crowd in on an already pre-occupied mind, leaving the sufferer in a highly sensitive and vulnerable state.

Lay people often trot out the old 'Pull yourself together' advice at this point. This is the last thing the sufferer needs – if they were capable of 'pulling themselves together' they would. Whilst well-meaning family members and friends may offer such advice in good faith, a person who is racked by fears and anxieties needs professional help.

Whilst these pages and the Phobias Interchange are here to help, I am not a doctor and so the first port of call is your GP. There are manifestations of anxiety which can be confused with physical ailments so it is necessary to establish that your problems are mentally driven and are not caused or being exacerbated by any physical problem.

Whilst it is true that doctors are busy people, there is no question of your problem being trivialised or ridiculed. Recent research has shown that anxiety-related problems are very real and so, in the highly unlikely event that your GP is unhelpful, you have every right to see another.

To be fair to your GP, it is important to make a short list of your experiences, together with any questions you may have. This will prevent anything which might be of importance being forgotten in the heat of the moment.

Lastly, there is one point which is very important to the sufferer, a point which crops up again and again in consultations. Many ask, 'Am I going mad?' The short answer is no. Insanity is not a consequence of anxiety disorders, even though it may some-times seem so.

• The above is an extract from the web site www.psychomotor.co.uk

All about depression

Information for those wanting to know more about depression

Introduction

This information is for anyone who wants to know more about depression. You may be experiencing depression yourself and wondering where to find help. You may be supporting a friend or relative who seems to be depressed, or you may work with people who have symptoms of depression – for example in a healthcare setting or a workplace. This article will give you information about depression and the kinds of help which are available. Included is some extra information on depression in older people, since depression in this age group is often overlooked.

The message of this article is that depression is a common and serious mental health problem, but there are many ways of helping people with depression to recover and resume happy and fulfilling lives. The more information you have, the

By Dr Jo Borrill, Clinical Research Manager, the Mental Health Foundation

better you will be able to ask for the help you need.

What is depression?

The word depression is used to describe a range of moods – from low spirits to a severe problem that interferes with everyday life. People who are experiencing severe or 'clinical' depression are not just sad or upset. The experience of depression is an overwhelming feeling which can make someone feel quite unable to cope, and hopeless about the future. If you are depressed you may lose your appetite and have difficulty sleeping. You can feel overwhelmed by guilt, and may even find yourself thinking about death or suicide. There is often an overlap between anxiety and depression, in that if you are depressed you may also become anxious or agitated.

Sometimes it is difficult to decide whether someone is responding 'normally' to difficult times, or has become clinically depressed. A rough guide in this situation is that 'if your low mood affects all parts of your life (home, work, family, social activities), lasts for two weeks or more, and brings you to the point of thinking about suicide' (BMA 1998) then you may be experiencing clinical depression and you should seek some kind of help.

Who becomes depressed?

Anyone can become depressed. Approximately one person in six experiences depression of some kind in the course of their lifetime and 1 in 20 experiences clinical depression. At any one time, about one in 10 people will have some symptoms of depression. Of course, people who are depressed do not always seek help and even if they do, they may not always be diagnosed as depressed, so these figures are only estimates.

People from all backgrounds, ages and cultures can experience depression, although people vary in how they express their difficulties. In many Western countries women are more likely then men to be diagnosed with depression, but this is partly because men are less likely to report their depression and seek help.

Children and young people
About 2% of children under 12 experience depression. This rises to about 5% for teenagers. A particular worry is the rise in the numbers of young men who attempt suicide, which is often the result of depression.

Adults
Depression in both women and men is often linked to life changes or to loneliness. About 10% of women experience post-natal depression in the weeks following childbirth. Social factors which can make people more at risk of becoming depressed include loss of employment, bereavement and problems with relationships.

Older adults
People over 65 seem to have a slightly greater risk of depression. This risk gets much higher in people over 85 years. It can be particularly difficult to recognise depression in older people because they are less likely to talk about feeling sad or low, and more likely to talk about physical problems such as loss of energy or difficulty sleeping. This means that GPs, family and friends may not understand how they are feeling. In older people it appears that depression is less likely to 'lift' without help, particularly if they are severely depressed. This may explain why older depressed people have a high suicide rate, particularly men over the age of 75 years.

Depression can also be confused with the effects of other health problems, which are more common in later life. People who are depressed often report feeling confused and having difficulty in thinking and remembering things.

In older people it is important to find out whether these problems are due to depression or to the development of dementia – for example in Alzheimer's disease or following a stroke.

How is depression diagnosed?
When deciding whether to give someone a diagnosis of depression, professionals look for the following key symptoms:

- Depressed or irritable mood most of the day, nearly every day
- Loss of interest or pleasure
- Changes in weight or appetite
- Sleep problems
- Agitation
- Tiredness and loss of energy
- Feeling guilty or worthless
- Difficulty in concentrating or making decisions
- Thoughts of death or suicide

A diagnosis of depression should be given if you experience at least five of these symptoms over a two-week period. However, everybody's experience of being depressed is different. For example, some people are severely depressed for a relatively short time while others have milder depression over a number of years, and there are other patterns in between. Even if the depression seems mild it is still important, and can have a big impact on someone's life and ability to enjoy life.

We also need to understand that there are differences in the way people describe their feelings. For example, some people use words such as 'sad' or 'low' to describe feeling depressed, whereas other people describe their feelings in terms of their body, such as 'a pain in my heart'.

Are there different kinds of depression?
The following are some specific types of depression which have been identified:

Bipolar disorder (Manic depression)
About 1% of the population will experience bipolar disorder at some time in their lives. A diagnosis of bipolar disorder means that you have both 'high' and 'low' mood swings, along with changes in thoughts, emotions and physical health. The mood swings are normally more extreme than everyday ups and downs. This kind of depression is sometimes also referred to as manic depression. Most people with bipolar disorder have their first episode of depression in their late teens or early twenties, and without treatment it is very likely to recur.

Post-natal depression
About 10 to 15% of women experience post-natal depression in the first year after having a baby.

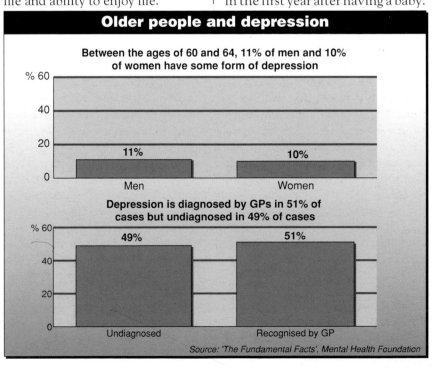

Older people and depression

Between the ages of 60 and 64, 11% of men and 10% of women have some form of depression

Men: 11%
Women: 10%

Depression is diagnosed by GPs in 51% of cases but undiagnosed in 49% of cases

Undiagnosed: 49%
Recognised by GP: 51%

Source: 'The Fundamental Facts', Mental Health Foundation

They may be unusually tearful, anxious or irritable, and may also find it difficult to play with their babies and respond positively to them. Although most women feel 'up and down' in the first few days of childbirth – the so-called 'baby blues' – because of rapid hormone changes, post-natal depression is very different from this and lasts longer.

It is probably due to a mixture of biological, psychological and social factors, and women are particularly at risk of post-natal depression if they do not have a supportive partner or family to help them. If someone seems to be showing signs of post-natal depression their Health Visitor should be able to assess them and provide appropriate help. Most women with post-natal depression benefit greatly from supportive counselling and from talking to other women who have been through a similar experience.

Seasonal affective disorder (SAD)
Some people describe feeling depressed regularly at certain times of the year. Usually this kind of depression starts in the autumn or winter, when daylight is reduced. Because of this a popular treatment for SAD is the use of special bright light. A key feature of this kind of depression is the desire to sleep more and eat carbohydrate foods. People experiencing this kind of depression may be helped by specially designed light boxes.

What causes depression?
There are many possible causes of depression. You may have an increased risk of experiencing depression because of your particular biological make-up. On the other hand, depression is also related to what is happening in your life, and the kind of support you receive from others. Past experiences which may be difficult or traumatic, such as losing a parent when very young, can affect your ability to ability to cope with difficult situations.

Is depression inherited?
There is some evidence that depression seems to run in families, but there is no single gene which causes depression. A family history of depression may increase the risk, but this may be because of difficulties the family has in coping, and it certainly does not mean that depression is inevitable. Genes seem to be more important than childhood experiences in determining the risk of bipolar disorder.

Is depression caused by changes in the brain?
We know that depression is associated with changes in the activity of certain brain chemicals, known as 'neurotransmitters', which affect our mood and thinking. These chemicals, such as serotonin, are also affected by factors such as activity and exercise. Drug treatment aims to restore 'normal' levels of neurotransmitter activity.

What about stress?
An episode of depression can be 'triggered' by stressful things that happen in our lives, particularly events involving a loss of some kind – such as unemployment, leaving home, death of a family member or friend. Even an apparently happy event can also bring a sense of loss; for example, parents can feel they have 'lost' their son or daughter when they get married, even if they are very happy for them. If you have had to cope with a lot of changes or stressful events, one more may seem like the 'last straw'.

Older people may have to cope with repeated losses, and are particularly likely to experience bereavement. A study of people in their 70s found that those whose husbands or wives had recently died were four times more likely to be depressed than those who were still married. Some widows and widowers still had high levels of depression two years after the death of their spouse. Men living alone after the death of their wives seem to be particularly at risk for depression.

Styles of thinking and coping
Everyone has to deal with sadness, disappointment and loss at some time in their life. But whether this leads to depression can depend on your ability to adopt a hopeful approach to life. People who are depressed tend to think about bad experiences in ways that make them even more difficult to manage.

If you have had bad experiences in the past, which you were unable to control, you develop a 'hopeless' way of thinking. Feeling 'trapped' in a difficult situation or experiencing a feeling of humiliation can also lead to negative thinking and depression. But . . .

Health and illness
We all tend to feel feel miserable when we are ill. But long-term health problems, which prevent someone from leading their usual life, may lead to depression. People who lose their eyesight or hearing can become depressed, as can people with heart disease, chronic lung diseases, and illnesses which prevent them from getting about, such as Parkinson's disease or stroke.

Family and friends can help a lot, by helping people find new activities or interests following illness.

Is it 'normal' to become depressed as you get older?
It is usual to experience sadness, grief, and disappointment when we encounter difficulties or losses. Some of these life events may become more common with age, for example, when children move away, family members die, or friends become ill or disabled. Health or financial problems can undoubtedly add to the burdens of age. However, it is important that severe (clinical) depression is recognised, so that people can get the help they need. Many people find that there are positive benefits of growing older, such as having more free time, being able to take up hobbies or spend time with grandchildren, or getting away from a stressful working life. It is therefore wrong to assume that depression in older people is a 'normal' reaction to growing older.

• The above is an extract from the text of a booklet published by the Mental Health Foundation. See page 41 for address details.

© 2000 Mental Health Foundation

Depression in children and young people

How to recognise and help

What is depression?

Most people – children as well as adults – have felt low for short spells from time to time. Feeling 'depressed' or sad is a normal reaction to experiences that are stressful, upsetting or difficult to come to terms with.

But when depression goes on and on, when it is so bad that it dominates and interferes with your whole life – it can become an illness. This is much less common. It probably affects 1 in every 200 children under 12 years old and 2-3 in every 100 teenagers. It is more common in adults. When depression reaches the point of becoming an illness, it needs treatment.

What are the signs of depression?

- Being moody and irritable – easily upset, 'ratty' or tearful.
- Becoming withdrawn – avoiding friends, family and regular activities.
- Feeling guilty or bad, being self-critical and self-blaming – hating yourself.
- Feeling unhappy, miserable and lonely a lot of the time.
- Feeling hopeless and wanting to die.
- Difficulty concentrating.
- Not looking after your personal appearance.
- Difficulty getting off to sleep or waking very early.
- Tiredness and lack of energy.
- Frequent minor health problems such as headaches or stomach-aches.

If you have all or most of these signs for a long time, it may mean that you are depressed.

What effects can depression have?

Because depression affects so many aspects of life – your outlook, how you feel, what you are able to do – this can make it hard for you to cope with ordinary daily life as well as usual. For example, depression can cause:

- difficulties getting on with friends and family.
- loss of friends.
- loss of confidence, difficulty making decisions.
- inability to study, work and do well in exams.
- difficulty getting up in the morning and facing the day.
- eating problems – turning to food for comfort and eating too much, or dieting excessively.

Depression can sometimes be dangerous, increasing the risk of:

- self-injury – e.g. drug overdoses, self-cutting.
- suicide.
- drug, alcohol or solvent misuse.

A young person who is depressed will often feel unable to talk about these difficulties unless they are directly asked about them.

What causes depression?

Depression is usually caused by a mixture of things, rather than any one thing alone.

Events or personal experiences can trigger depression. These include family breakdown, the death or loss of a loved one, neglect, abuse and bullying and physical illness. It can also be triggered if too many changes happen in your life too quickly.

Risk factors

People are more at risk of becoming depressed if they are under a lot of stress, have no one to share their worries with, and lack practical support. Past events, such as the death of a parent in childhood, being abused or neglected as a child can also increase the risk of depression.

Biological factors

Depression often runs in families due to genetic factors. Someone with a close relative who suffers from depression has a higher than normal risk of becoming depressed themselves. Girls and women are more likely than boys and men to suffer from depression.

Depression seems to be linked with chemical changes in the part of the brain that controls mood. These changes prevent normal functioning of the brain and cause many of the symptoms.

What can help?
There are a lot of things that can be done to help people who suffer from depression.

Helping yourself
Simply sharing worries with someone who understands can lighten the burden. It can also make it easier to work out practical solutions to problems. Often, depression is connected with a particular problem which needs practical help from professionals. For example, if you are stressed out by exams, you should talk to your teacher or school counsellor. If you are worried about being pregnant, you should go and see your general practitioner or family planning clinic.

Do
- talk to someone who can help.
- keep as active and occupied as possible.
- remember: you are not alone – depression is a common problem and can be overcome.

How parents and teachers can help
It can be very hard for young people to put their feelings into words. You can help by asking sympathetically how they are feeling and listening. Reassurance and advice may be very

helpful. Teenagers who are depressed may feel very sensitive to being patronised or fobbed off. It's important not to take this too personally. You can show that you take them seriously by offering space to think about how difficulties can be overcome. Encouraging them to keep active and praising their efforts can make a huge difference.

When specialist help is needed
If the depression is dragging on and causing serious difficulties, it's important to seek treatment. Your family doctor will be able to advise you about what help is available and to arrange a referral to the local child and adolescent mental health service. Usually, these specialist teams consist of psychiatrists, psychologists, psychotherapists and social workers, all of whom are highly skilled in

helping young people and their families. A child and adolescent psychiatrist is a medically qualified doctor who is trained to diagnose depression and to help with practical and effective ways of overcoming it.

The most effective forms of treatment include cognitive therapy and antidepressant medication (see Royal College's Patient Factsheets on these topics). If someone is severely depressed, antidepressant medication may help them to recover more quickly. Antidepressants are thought to act by correcting the chemical changes in the brain. There are a number of different types of antidepressant, each of which works in slightly different ways. Your psychiatrist will be able to discuss which one would be the most suitable. Antidepressants take a few weeks to work, and usually need to be taken for several months. They are non-addictive. Side-effects of the modern antidepressants are usually mild and lessen as treatment goes on.

• The above information is from the Royal College of Psychiatrists' web site which can be found at www.rcpsych.org.uk Alternatively, see page 41 for their address details.
© *Royal College of Psychiatrists*

Postnatal depression

Information from the Association for Postnatal Illness

Introduction
Most people today have heard the term 'baby blues' used to describe a mild short, period of depression which many women experience after childbirth. Fewer people are aware that as many as 10% of all recently delivered women develop postnatal depression. In a proportion of these mothers the depression may be of such severity that they need out-patient psychiatric help and many need drug therapy.

In view of its common occurrence it is surprising that postnatal depression is so rarely mentioned in books about pregnancy and

childbirth, and it is not usually discussed in ante-natal classes.

The purpose of this information is to give some information about the many symptoms of postnatal depression, from the mildest to the most severe forms. The list of symptoms should not alarm you, women who experience depression will probably recognise a combination of symptoms which apply to their particular case. Do remember that this is a condition which always results in complete recovery, and the distressing symptoms can be abolished by drug therapy.

Sadly, many mothers experience severe depression without recognising it as a treatable illness. This can mean the mother suffering needless distress and can also affect her family and friends. If a mother can recognise her condition then she may seek medical help at an earlier stage of the illness.

After the birth
The 'baby blues' usually arrive within the first week after the birth of the baby. The mother may feel very emotional and find that she keeps bursting into tears. She cannot explain why she is upset, and is not

easily cheered up. She should be allowed to cry and not admonished for being weepy and miserable.

Sometimes the mother feels confused and unable to concentrate, she may read a book but be unable to follow the story. Often her memory becomes very bad and many mothers worry about this.

The 'blues' may be connected with sudden hormone changes that occur when a women gives birth.

There are factors other than the 'baby blues' which can make a mother feel depressed after the birth. Many newborn babies have a degree of jaundice or some feeding difficulties in the first week; as these conditions improve the mother will feel happier.

A new mother may feel that she will be unable to cope when at home alone with the baby. This is especially the case with first-time mothers. Often the promise of practical help from family and friends can ease the situation, and as the mother learns how to cope at home her feelings of depression lift.

If the mother is worrying about her ability to support the baby financially she can get advice from the social worker in hospital or from her health visitor and local DHSS when she returns home. Many mothers are unaware of the range of benefits to which they are entitled once they have had a baby.

Symptoms of tension, anxiety, sleeping difficulties and poor appetite are very common just after a woman has given birth but they are usually so mild that the mother can live a normal, happy and active life when she returns home. It is, however, terribly important that a new mother should get as much rest as possible, especially if she is experiencing a mild patch of the 'blues'. She should make sure that she has at least one proper rest, in bed, every day, until the baby is several weeks old

In a few cases the 'blues' get worse and symptoms become more distressing. In this case a mother should see her doctor as soon as possible, as this is a common and treatable condition.

Developing depression
Slowly developing postnatal depression can take two forms. One

type occurs when a patch of postnatal 'blues' which started soon after the baby's birth becomes worse and more and more distressing as time passes. The second type develops more slowly and is not noticeable until several weeks after the birth of the baby.

Depression
Many mothers begin to feel depressed, increasingly despondent and hopeless soon after the baby is born. They may feel terribly miserable and sad for no particular reason and may find that they spend a large part of each day in tears. Sometimes the mother may feel rejected by her partner, family, friends, or even by the new baby; these feelings usually have no foundation. The depressed mother may feel permanently tired and lethargic, unable to cope with household chores. She may give up bathing, dressing properly or making up.

Sometimes the care of the baby is too much for the mother whilst she is unwell and someone else must be found to 'take over' until she has recovered. It is usually inadvisable to separate the mother from her baby, as this may serve to deepen the depression. If a relation or friend cannot be found to keep the mother company and help look after the baby, an advertisement may be placed in a local paper for a lively pensioner who for a small fee will help a convalescent mother with a young baby. This arrangement enables the mother to stay in her own home and keep her baby with her whilst she recovers.

Anxiety
A depressed mother may feel extremely anxious about a variety of subjects and situations. She may be worried about her health, possibly having felt unwell since the birth of the baby. She may experience severe pain for which the doctor can find no satisfactory explanation. This pain is often in the head or neck. Other mothers suffer backache, and chest pains which they fear are due to heart trouble. The mother may have a number of minor medical complaints which can cause undue distress.

Pain and a general feeling of illness or constant tiredness are very common symptoms of depression and can become worse if the depression remains untreated.

Anxiety may take the form of unjustified worries about the health and well-being of other members of the family, especially the baby.

The mother may feel too tense and anxious to go out of her home. She may not be able to bear to meet even her closest friends, and may refuse to answer the door, telephone or letters. In this situation she will not venture out to consult a doctor so a home visit may be required.

Panic

A depressed mother is often very confused by everyday situations and may experience feelings of panic. These feelings are unpredictable and often very distressing. She is unable to 'calm down' and every effort should be made to avoid the situations in which she becomes distressed.

Tension

Feelings of tension are often associated with depression. The mother who experiences these feelings finds them extremely distressing. She is quite unable to 'relax' however much she is encouraged to do so. She may feel as if she is about to explode when the tension is at its worst. This type of tension, when it is a symptom of depression, may not be helped by taking tranquillisers. Women taking these drugs should not despair if they do not work, as there are other drugs, which run no risk of dependency, that can be of more help.

Obsessional and inappropriate thoughts

A mother suffering from depression commonly has some obsessional thoughts. These may be about a person, a situation or about a certain activity. Some mothers become very frightened and believe that they may harm a member of their family especially the baby. These fears are very common symptoms of depression and may or may not be accompanied by feelings of guilt. Such fears are almost entirely unjustified, but if a mother is afraid that she may hurt the baby then she should tell her family and doctor.

A distressed mother may find the companionship of a suitable relative or friend reassuring. This phase of illness usually passes quickly once treatment has started to have its effect. The mother will benefit from the company and moral support of a companion as she recovers.

Concentration

A depressed mother will probably find that she cannot concentrate on books, television programmes or even conversation. She will find, to her distress, that her memory is very poor and she will often feel very dis-

organised. She will find that she sits for long periods of time doing nothing, but thinking about how awful she feels.

Sleeping

Often a depressed mother will have some form of sleeping difficulty. She may be awake until the early hours of the morning, or get no sleep at all. Some find that they sleep very fitfully and waken frequently, others that they wake in the early hours of the morning with nightmares, and then cannot get back to sleep.

Many depressed mothers dread going to bed as their symptoms trouble them more at night. Indeed some mothers find insomnia one of the most distressing aspects of the illness. Often mothers are prescribed sleeping pills by their GP and find them ineffective even taken in large doses. This situation can cause the mother to feel quite desperate. If the depression is treated normal sleep will be restored.

The feeding requirements of a young baby do not help a mother who is having sleeping difficulties. It can be of great benefit if someone else can feed the baby at night

Sex

A common effect of depression is complete loss of interest in sex. This may last for some time, and it is helpful if partners realise that this is a symptom of the illness and that sexual desire will return as soon as the depression lifts. It should be stressed that a return of sexual desire is often the last sign that a depression has lifted, and great patience is necessary if a relationship is to be kept intact whilst a mother recovers from postnatal depression.

During the illness physical contact in the form of touching, hugging and cuddling can do much to reassure both partners and is very beneficial.

There are many other symptoms of depression but these are some of the most common and show how this condition can manifest itself in various ways.

How the family can help

Firstly friends or family should make sure that the depressed mother is receiving treatment for her depression from the doctor. If the treatment she is prescribed does not suit her, do encourage her to go back to the doctor and ask him to change it. It can be helpful if someone accompanies the mother when she sees the doctor. This person can then assure the doctor that the mother is ill and not just being 'nervy'.

The family should understand that the illness is a temporary one, and that with their help and support the mother will recover. They should realise that it may take a considerable period of time before she is completely better.

Please do forget all ideas of 'chivvying' her out of it and accept that she is unwell. Try to treat her as you would if she had a simple physical illness.

When she is feeling unwell, take on as much of the running of the household as she wants to give up. However when she feels better let her do as much as she wants to. You may find that she has patches of good and bad days, this is very common with the illness.

Do remind her constantly that she will get better. Remember that depression is not a sign of weakness; Winston Churchill suffered from it.

Often a depressed mother will hate being left alone. If this is so, then try to organise a rota so that there is *always* someone who is close to her, and whom she trusts in attendance. This is a passing phase of the illness but it is most important that help is given until the mother is happy to be left on her own.

Ultimately anything you can do to help the mother through the distressing stages of this illness will help her towards recovery.

© The Association for Postnatal Illness

Seasonal affective disorder

Information from the SAD Association (SADA)

What is SAD?

SAD (Seasonal Affective Disorder) is a type of depression which affects an estimated half a million people every winter between September and April, in particular during December, January and February. It is caused by a biochemical imbalance in the hypothalamus due to the shortening of daylight hours and the lack of sunlight in winter. For many people SAD is a seriously disabling illness, preventing them from functioning normally without continuous medical treatment. For others, it is mild but debilitating condition causing discomfort but not severe illness, which we call sub-syndromal SAD or winter blues.

Symptoms

The symptoms of SAD usually recur regularly each winter, starting between September and November and continuing until March or April, and a diagnosis can be made after three or more consecutive winters of symptoms, which include a number of the following:

- Sleep problems, usually desire to oversleep and difficulty staying awake but, in some cases, disturbed sleep and early morning wakening.
- Lethargy, feeling of fatigue and inability to carry out normal routine.
- Overeating, craving for carbohydrates and sweet foods, usually resulting in weight gain.
- Depression, feelings of misery, guilt and loss of self-esteem, sometimes hopelessness and despair, sometimes apathy and loss of feelings.
- Social problems, irritability and desire to avoid social contact.
- Anxiety, tension and inability to tolerate stress.
- Loss of libido, decreased interest in sex and physical contact.
- Mood change, in some sufferers, extremes of mood and short periods of hypomania (over-activity) in spring and autumn.

Most sufferers show signs of a weakened immune system during the winter, and are more vulnerable to infections and other illness. SAD symptoms disappear in spring, either suddenly with a short period (e.g. four weeks) of hypomania or hyper-activity, or gradually depending on the intensity of sunlight in the spring and early summer. In sub-syndromal SAD, symptoms such as tiredness, lethargy, sleep and eating problems occur, but depression and anxiety are absent or mild. SAD may begin at any age but the main age of onset is 18-30. It occurs throughout the northern and southern hemispheres but is extremely rare in those living within 30 degrees of the Equator, where daylight hours are long, constant and extremely bright.

Treatment

Light therapy has been proved effective in up to 85% of diagnosed cases, that is, exposure for up to four hours per day (average 1-2 hours) to very bright light, at least ten times the intensity of ordinary domestic lighting. Ordinary light bulbs and fittings are not strong enough. Average domestic or office lighting emits an intensity of 200-500 lux but the minimum dose necessary to treat SAD is 2500 lux. The intensity of a bright summer day can be 100,000lux!

Light treatment should be used daily in winter (and dull periods in summer), starting in early autumn when the first symptoms appear. It consists of sitting two to three feet away from a specially designed light box, usually on a table, allowing the light to shine directly through the eyes. The user can carry out normal activity while stationary in front of the box, reading, working, eating, knitting etc. It is not necessary to stare at the light although it has been proved safe. Treatment is usually effective within three or four days and the effect continues provided it is used every day. Tinted lenses, or any device which blocks the light to the retina of the eye, should not be worn.

Some light boxes emit higher intensity of light, up to 10,000 lux, which can cut treatment time down to half an hour a day. Light boxes are not available on the NHS and have to be bought from specialist retailers; they are free of VAT for medical treatment and start at less than £100. SADA recommends trying before buying; most companies offer a home trial or hire scheme and SADA has a number of boxes for short-term hire.

Traditional antidepressant drugs such as tricyclics are not usually helpful for SAD as they exacerbate the sleepiness and lethargy which

are symptoms of the illness. The SSRI drugs, e.g. sertraline (Lustral), paroxetine (Seroxat) and SNRI drugs, e.g. venlafaxine (Efexor) alleviate the depressive symptoms of SAD and combine well with light therapy. Other psychotropic drugs, e.g.lithium, benzodiazepines, have not proved widely useful in the treatment of SAD. Daily exposure to as much natural daylight as possible, especially at midday, should help. Psychotherapy, counselling or any complementary therapy which helps the sufferer to relax, accept their illness and cope with its limitations are extremely useful. Full details of SAD treatment, where to obtain it and how to use it are contained in the SADA information pack.

SAD Association

The SAD Association is a voluntary organisation and registered charity which informs the public and health professions about SAD and supports and advises sufferers of the illness. It produces a newsletter three times a year and other publications, holds meetings, has a network of contacts and local groups, a lightbox hire scheme and raises money for research into SAD. SADA receives no funding so has to charge for the information and membership.

Further information and membership of SADA

You can send for the SADA information pack which contains full details of SAD treatments, where to obtain light therapy equipment and how to use it, how to hire light fixtures and try out light treatment, how to adapt your lifestyle, clinics, meetings, books, research updates and GP information OR you can enrol as a member of SADA and receive an information pack and a year's membership with newsletters, list of contacts, telephone helpline, local groups, research and treatment updates, invitations to meetings, reduced rate books and other goods.
© SADA

All about dementia

Information for those wanting to know more about dementia

What is dementia?

Dementia is a gradual decline in mental ability:

- memory
- thinking
- problem-solving
- concentrating
- perception.

It has many forms, and often we do not know what causes it although as described (see 'What causes dementia?' below) we have some ideas. There are other problems sometimes associated with dementia which can often be successfully treated. These include things like

- depression
- sleep problems
- aggression
- inappropriate sexual behaviour
- incontinence.

What is the difference between dementia and Alzheimer's disease? How common are they?

Alzheimer's disease is an illness of which the main symptom is dementia, and it accounts for about 60% of the cases of dementia diagnosed. It was named after Alois Alzheimer, a German doctor who first described it, in 1907.

Alzheimer's disease cannot be diagnosed with total certainty during

---

By Dr Sophie Zerman, Scientific Officer at the Mental Health Foundation

---

someone's lifetime. It is characterised by damage ('plaques' and 'tangles') seen in and around brain cells when these are examined at a post-mortem.

Other forms of dementia differ in terms of their symptoms, causes and the precise changes in the brain (see 'In what other diseases as well as Alzheimer's does dementia occur?' opposite).

People with all forms of dementia differ in terms of which signs and symptoms they have and the speed and extent to which their illnesses progress – problems vary, even day to day. This article is intended as a general guide – not all the problems will be relevant to everyone. Despite this, those with all types of dementia are likely to need similar care and support and hence this information is relevant to the range of diagnoses.

What causes dementia?

Dementia occurs as a result of death of cells or damage in parts of the brain that deal with our thought processes. This may follow other problems like:

- lack of blood and therefore oxygen supply to these brain areas
- head injury
- pressure (such as from a tumour)
- infection (such as in AIDS).

In some cases, therefore, we can identify what is likely to be causing dementia, and indeed treat the problem. In others – those with Alzheimer's disease, for example – we do not know why brain cells become 'sick', although this is the focus of intense research.

After Alzheimer's disease, the second most common type is vascular dementia, which occurs as a result of lack of blood and oxygen to the brain in a series of tiny 'strokes'. Other types of dementia are rarer, and may be due to:

- Lewy body disease
- Pick's disease
- Huntingdon's disease or chorea
- Creutzfeld Jakob disease (CJD), the human equivalent of 'mad cow disease'
- dementia as part of a neurological (brain) illness such as Parkinson's
- a brain tumour
- fluid build-up (hydrocephalus)
- a long period of excessive alcohol intake.

These last three causes are to some extent treatable, as is the dementia that may result from causes such as vitamin or hormone deficiency or syphilis. These possibilities should always be investigated.

In what other diseases as well as Alzheimer's disease does dementia occur?

The second most common cause of dementia after Alzheimer's disease is vascular dementia. 'Multi-infarct' dementia is the most common sort, in which cells in certain regions of the brain die because the blood supply to them is poor. Risk factors for this are the same as those for stroke. Dementia progresses gradually – characteristically capacity for learning, memory, speech and language decreases, and people may have more insight into their condition than do those with Alzheimer's disease. Other distinctive features may include:
- marked emotional swings
- night-time confusion
- fits like those of epilepsy
- partial or total paralysis of a limb.

Another characteristic form of dementia is related to the presence of 'Lewy bodies' – tiny spherical structures found inside brain cells, which may cause them to die. About a quarter of people with Alzheimer's disease are found to have Lewy bodies in their brain cells when they are examined after death. They are also found in brain cells affected by Parkinson's disease (PD), in which the ability to control movement is impaired. Researchers disagree as to whether diffuse Lewy body disease is a distinct condition or a variant of Alzheimer's disease or PD, and indeed dementia linked to the presence of Lewy bodies is known by many names. Symptoms vary, and may be indistinguishable from those of Alzheimer's disease, or more mild in the early stages. Movement disorders like those of PD may occur in parallel with dementia, and the severity of dementia, confusion and hallucinations that some people experience may be quite variable, even from hour to hour.

The main difference between Pick's disease and Alzheimer's disease is that, in their early stages at least, damage occurs in different brain areas. That most commonly first affected in Pick's disease is the front,

and dementias of this origin are thus sometimes referred to as 'frontal lobe dementia'.

Early signs may be:
- changes in personality
- impaired judgement
- lack of inhibition
- reduced speech
- obsessional behaviour.

And if the disease includes cell death in the brain's temporal lobes, prominent signs include
- memory loss
- difficulties with object recognition
- changes in eating habits – gorging, and often craving sweet food.

The age of onset is most commonly between 40 and 65 years.

Dementia and younger people

There are two distinct ways in which younger people may experience dementia – through witnessing it in elderly relatives, or, extremely rarely, developing it themselves. The vast majority of young people affected by dementia see it develop in grandparents or other elderly relatives.

Explaining the illness to them can be very difficult, and the Alzheimer's Disease Society has produced leaflets on this. A distinction used to be made between dementia occurring in those above 60 and those under, with the term 'pre-senile dementia' sometimes applied to the latter.

Treatable causes of dementia

It is important to rule out conditions which could be treated to reverse or stop progression of dementia. The following categories summarise the main dementias of this sort:

- **Head injury-related**

Internal bleeding after a head injury can lead to a clot that presses on the brain and in turn causes dementia. Such subdural haematomas can often be surgically removed.

Another problem that can occur after head injury is a build-up of cerebrospinal fluid (CSF), which normally protects and cushions the brain. Internal bleeding and infections can also cause this hydrocephalous which may be noticed first as problems with walking and incontinence. Again, surgical treatment can help.

- **Dietary**

While long-term alcohol abuse can itself damage the brain and cause dementia, people who abuse alcohol may also neglect their food intake and become deficient in certain vitamins and minerals. Improving diet and stopping drinking can help. Korsakoff's syndrome, often manifest as memory loss, can occur after prolonged heavy drinking due to vitamin B1 (thiamine) deficiency.

Vitamin deficiency alone, especially lack of B1, 3, 6 and 12, can

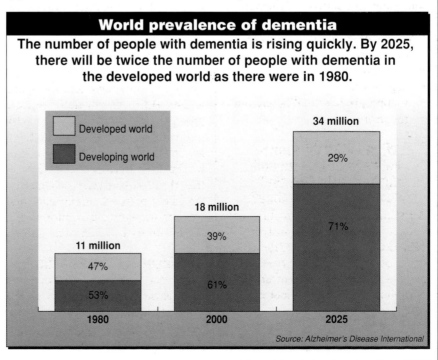

World prevalence of dementia
The number of people with dementia is rising quickly. By 2025, there will be twice the number of people with dementia in the developed world as there were in 1980.

Developed world
Developing world

11 million
47%
53%
1980

18 million
39%
61%
2000

34 million
29%
71%
2025

Source: Alzheimer's Disease International

cause dementia-like symptoms. A simple blood test and vitamin supplements can help.

• *Dementia linked to other illnesses*
An underactive thyroid gland (hypothyroidism) can lead to dementia which may be reversible by replacing thyroid hormone (thyroxine). The chances of this working well are increased if the problem is recognised within two years.

Other treatable hormone problems may lead to dementia, as can conditions such as systemic lupus erythematosus (SLE), syphilis and brain tumours. Reduction of the blood supply to the brain due to cardiac or respiratory failure or anaemia may also be to some extent treatable. Finally, it is worth remembering that a dementia-like illness can occur in elderly people who are severely depressed, and this possibility should always be investigated.

Is dementia inherited?
Most studies looking into whether dementia runs in the family have been on Alzheimer's disease, and most cases do not. Those that do tend to begin quite young – if at least three people from one side of a family have developed Alzheimer's disease between 36 and 60, there may be a genetic predisposition to it. Although it is by no means inevitable that you will develop it, you may want to ask your GP to refer you to a genetic counsellor or a specialist dementia clinic.

• The above is an extract from the booklet *All about Dementia*, which is published by the Mental Health Foundation. See page 41 for address details.

Half of GPs ignore need for early diagnosis of dementia

By David Brindle, Social Services Correspondent

One in two family doctors believes it unimportant to make an early diagnosis of dementia in elderly people because it is seen as untreatable and its diagnosis alone can cause great distress, the audit commission reports today.

Only half of all carers of people with dementia say they were told about the diagnosis soon after their relative or friend started to become confused, and fewer still were advised how it might affect them or asked if they needed any help.

Whether dementia is regarded as treatable or not, the commission says, carers deserve early information and support. A clear diagnosis can also trigger help from community services, sometimes deferring or even preventing admission to residential care.

Andrew Foster, the commission's controller, said: 'It is unacceptable that carers, who are so essential to vulnerable older people, can find themselves forgotten by the system.'

A report by the commission, based on study of 12 areas of the country, says mental health services for elderly people are 'patchy and inconsistent'. Spending on specialist services for problems such as dementia and depression varies from area to area by as much as eight to one and is too heavily skewed towards residential care, it says.

Calling for urgent action to make services more consistent and comprehensive, the commission is warning that the over-80s are one of the fastest growing groups of the population and that one in four of those over 85 will develop dementia.

In the first move of its kind, the commission is to send auditors into every district in England and Wales during this year and next to check on the level and quality of services, and, specifically, how different health and welfare agencies liaise in their provision.

Mr Foster said: 'GPs and primary care teams could give far better information and support if they were

One GP commented: 'What is the point in looking for an untreatable illness?'

getting more help from specialist mental health professionals.' Research for the report, *Forget Me Not*, included a survey of more than 1,000 GPs. Although nine in 10 said it was important to look for early signs of depression in their elderly patients, only 54% said the same for dementia, while 52% believed it beneficial to make an early diagnosis of the condition.

One GP commented: 'What is the point in looking for an untreatable illness?' Another said: 'Diagnosing dementia can be difficult, uncertain and create unnecessary anxiety.'

A second survey, of 850 carers of people with dementia, found that barely 50% reported early diagnosis by a doctor. In one area, fewer than 30% said they had been asked if they needed any help coping with their relative's or friend's condition. The report describes these findings as 'rather worrying'.

The report was welcomed by groups working with elderly people and with those with mental health problems.

Gil Hitchon, chief executive of mental health charity Maca, said it was imperative that patients and carers were fully involved in decision making.

Common questions about Alzheimer's disease

The term dementia sometimes seems to be used instead of Alzheimer's disease. Are they two names for the same thing?

Dementia is a term used to describe various disorders of the brain that all result in progressive and severe loss of memory. Alzheimer's disease is the most common type of dementia, accounting on its own for approximately 50% of all cases (and occurring with another cause in a further 20% of cases). Alzheimer's disease also causes certain specific changes to the brain tissue (see the next answer).

People with Alzheimer's disease (and other dementias) gradually lose their sense of time and place. A major symptom is that they forget things that they have just said or done, although their memory for past events may for a time remain clear. As the disease progresses, people become unaware of their condition although they may still experience distress. They find it increasingly difficult and then impossible to perform even the simplest everyday tasks, including washing, eating and dressing, without supervision. They may become uncommunicative and incontinent, sometimes with severe behavioural problems. Most eventually need 24-hour care. The disease may go on for many years – typically between five and ten years – and tends not to be the eventual cause of death. More commonly, a person has Alzheimer's disease for many years before dying from something else, such as an infection or stroke.

Does Alzheimer's disease run in families?

Alzheimer's disease does sometimes run in families, but this is uncommon. Some rare cases of the disease, which tend to occur in people younger than usual, are known to be passed on in the genes from one generation to the next. In these cases, the probability that close family members (brothers, sisters and children) will develop Alzheimer's disease is one in two.

Most cases of Alzheimer's disease are not of the type that is passed on genetically. If a family member suffers from the non-genetic form of the disease, the risk to close relatives is around three times higher than the risk for a person of a similar age who has no family history of the disease. It is thought that in these cases a person's genes may contribute to the development of the disease but do not cause it directly.

How much is known about the possible causes of Alzheimer's disease?

This is an important area of current research, but at the present time a great deal still remains to be discovered about why people develop Alzheimer's disease. We know that Alzheimer's disease becomes more common with increasing age, but we don't know what factors trigger the characteristic changes that occur in the brain tissue of people who have this disease. We know that these brain changes are associated with ageing, but also that they are not part of the normal ageing process. In some cases, the changes occur at a relatively early age.

Genes are thought to play a part in the development of most cases of Alzheimer's disease. In rare cases, abnormal genes actually cause the disease. Much more commonly, genes are believed only to contribute to a person's susceptibility to the disease. It seems that, at least in some cases, factors in the environment may be necessary to trigger the illness.

Alzheimer's disease is certainly not infectious. Nor is it caused by over-use or under-use of the brain. Even though the disease is sometimes first noticed after a period of stress or worry, it is not thought that these emotions can actually cause the disease to develop. Nor is it believed that the trauma of an operation can trigger the disease. Claims are sometimes made that dietary or hormone deficiencies may contribute to the development of Alzheimer's disease, but

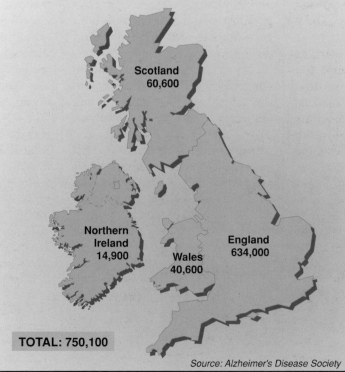

Statistics on dementia

The Alzheimer's Disease Society estimates that dementia currently (1998) affects over 700,000 people in the UK. Estimated numbers, using population figures for 1996:

Scotland 60,600

Northern Ireland 14,900

Wales 40,600

England 634,000

TOTAL: 750,100

Source: Alzheimer's Disease Society

most doctors do not accept these claims. Similarly, claims that aluminium in the diet may be a cause are not widely accepted.

How do the early symptoms of Alzheimer's disease differ from ordinary forgetfulness?

Many older people find that their memories are not as good as they used to be. For example, they have difficulty remembering people's names, things they were going to buy, or something they were going to do. This does not mean that they are getting Alzheimer's disease. A person who is ordinarily forgetful can still remember details associated with the thing they have forgotten. For example, they may briefly forget their next door neighbour's name but they still know that the person they are talking to is their neighbour. People with Alzheimer's disease forget not only details but the entire context. They may also have other problems, such as changes in behaviour and loss of ability to do everyday tasks.

How is Alzheimer's disease usually diagnosed?

A diagnosis of Alzheimer's disease is usually made on the basis of a patient's symptoms and mental abilities. To obtain as much information as possible, the doctor will undertake a process known as 'history taking', during which he or she will talk to the patient, and probably also to someone else who knows the patient well, such as a family member or friend.

There may also be a more formal assessment of a patient's physical and mental condition and needs. It is often difficult to make a conclusive diagnosis of Alzheimer's disease. Various other illnesses, such as depression, a thyroid problem, a vitamin deficiency or Parkinson's disease, can cause similar symptoms. A full physical examination, and various tests, including blood tests and perhaps a brain scan, can help rule out some of the other possibilities. If tests fail to show any other reason for a person's symptoms, a doctor will often make a diagnosis of Alzheimer's disease. Sometimes, the diagnosis is made only after observing how a patient's condition develops over a period of several months.

• The above information is from the publication *Alzheimer's at your Fingertips*, ISBN: 1 872363 71 0, priced at £11.95. It is available at a special UK price of £10.95 incl p&&p from Alzheimer's Disease Society. See page 41 for address details.

© *Alzheimer's Disease Society May, 2000*

What is schizophrenia?

Information from the National Schizophrenia Fellowship

Introduction

- Schizophrenia is an illness that can be treated.
- One in a hundred people will experience schizophrenia during their lifetime
- The majority of people with schizophrenia will lead ordinary lives

Schizophrenia is a mental illness. The first acute episode can be a devastating experience, particularly as both the person experiencing the illness and those close to him will be unprepared. About one in a hundred people world-wide experience at least one such episode at some time during their lives, although the highest incidence is in the late teens and early 20s. In about one-quarter of cases there is eventually a full recovery. The majority will have long periods of good functioning, with occasional problems. The recent discovery of new forms of treatment may lead to further improvement in rates of recovery, particularly if everyone involved, i.e. both the person with schizophrenia and their family, learns to understand how to cope.

In schizophrenia the activity of chemical messengers at certain nerve endings in the brain is unusual and this may be a clue to the causes of the disorder. During what is sometimes referred to as 'an acute episode' the mental processes of experiencing and thinking become distorted. When severe this can lead to intense panic, anger, depression, elation or over-activity, perhaps punctuated by periods of withdrawal. It is not surprising that other people, particularly family and friends, find the changes incomprehensible and are themselves devastated.

One common misconception is that schizophrenia is the result of 'split personality'. In fact 'multiple personality', the correct term, is very rare and has nothing to do with schizophrenia. The mistake comes from the fact that the name 'schizophrenia' was coined from two Greek words meaning 'split' and 'mind'. It was intended to represent the fact that processes of thought, feeling and intention, guiding the person's actions, no longer interact to form a coherent whole.

The symptoms of schizophrenia can be divided into two groups, called 'positive', e.g. hallucinations and delusions, and 'negative', e.g. slowness to move, think, speak or react. 'Positive' because these are new experiences and 'negative' because these are everyday parts of life, at a reduced level. These may occur together, separately or alternately. A person affected by schizophrenia may also experience secondary symptoms such as depression, as a result of the difficulties he may experience in learning to cope with day-to-day living.

Positive symptoms
a. Hallucinations

The positive symptoms are often based on new and rare experiences that most people who do not have schizophrenia never, or only in exceptional circumstances, have. Most commonly a person with schizophrenia will 'hear' his own thoughts, for example, as if they have been spoken aloud within his head.

The thoughts can appear to be so loud that the person may believe that people nearby will also be able to hear them. The mind usually adjusts to this very rapidly and as a result the thoughts then appear to come from some external source.

These spoken thoughts are then called 'voices' or, more technically, 'hallucinations'. The person may also experience sounds other than voices.

It is possible, using a medical imaging technique, to see changes in the speech area of the brain at the time when a person says that he is hearing the voices. This is a real experience, it is not imaginary. There can also be other kinds of hallucinations, visual, smell or taste.

b. Delusions
A person who experiences hallucination will naturally attempt to find an explanation for what is happening. Which kind of explanation they decide on depends very much on the person involved and the culture in which he lives.

The voices may, for example, be thought to come from the television. In a different culture, however, they may be put down to magic or given a religious explanation. These are attempts to make sense of experiences that most people do not have. To the outside world these explanations are regarded as delusions. Delusions can take many forms: persecutory, telepathic, grandiose, religious, sci-fi or para-normal. A person experiencing delusions may try to keep them secret, knowing that others would not understand. Other individuals are gradually overwhelmed and begin to act strangely according to the content of the delusional explanations.

Negative symptoms
In some cases, especially with hindsight, families may realise that their relative's behaviour has been changing over a period of time in subtle ways. He may for instance have become slower to think, talk and move, and may have become in-different to social contact, his sleeping patterns may have changed so that he is happy to remain up all night and sleep all day. Body language may also be affected. These are the so-called 'negative symptoms': they will affect the person in a different way from the positive symptoms. The overall result is a reduction of motivation, the effect of which varies from minor to severe. Negative symptoms are much less dramatic than positive, but they tend to be more persistent. Recognising these changes can be particularly difficult if the illness develops during teenage years when it is quite acceptable for changes in behaviour to occur, particularly where the young person is experimenting with new freedoms and lifestyles.

Secondary symptoms
Fortunately most people do not have both types of symptoms to a severe extent. However it is important to remember that the secondary symptoms accompanying schizophrenia, such as depression and demoralisation, may in themselves be disabling. The extent to which someone is affected by secondary symptoms depends in part on what kind of person they were before the onset of schizophrenia. There is an inter-action with earlier personality, education, intelligence and achievement. In addition, the reaction of the family members and friends will also have some impact, if, through misunderstanding, they think that their relative is fantasising, seeking attention or simply lying. Losing a job and possibly social contacts at work as a result of schizophrenia adds further problems.

Family and friends can provide a vital lifeline. It is essential to seek assistance for your relative as soon as symptoms appear. Treatment is most effective when it is given early and in the context of consistent and informed support from the family, who have also learned to understand schizophrenia.
© *National Schizophrenia Fellowship (NSF)*

Beginner's information about schizophrenia

Information from the Schizophrenia Association of Great Britain

Why should young people be interested in schizophrenia?
This information is about a disease, schizophrenia, which affects the delicate working of the brain and its neurotransmitters. As a result of the brain not working properly the behaviour, emotions and thinking of the person getting ill alters. The personality alters through disease.

A *friend or relation is becoming ill*
It is very difficult for others who are well to understand altered behaviour and thought in someone they have known for years. Why, they think, are they being horrible to me? Why are they so irritable, even angry, over nothing? Why are they so suspicious? Why do they look so ill?

You yourself are becoming ill
It really is horrible to become mentally ill. If the chemicals in your brain are not functioning properly it is very difficult not to be overwhelmed by pathological (the product of disease) thoughts coming into your head. You may become especially suspicious (paranoid) about your best friends and think they are trying to harm you. You may find it very difficult indeed to concentrate on what your tutor or your workmates are saying, and, as for remembering anything, it is quite a nightmare. You may get into trouble with the teacher

because your work has suddenly become so poor when previously you had always had good marks in tests. What is happening to you? You feel the whole world is against you and you just do not know why. You feel angry that no one is nice to you any more. Just let anyone tell you that you are bad tempered and you'll knock them for six. And what is that awful voice in your head telling you to do this and that in a most unpleasant way? How dictatorial it is! The voice seems to be real and yet no one else is there.

Psychiatric symptoms of mental illness

Just what is happening? The psychiatric symptoms by which schizophrenia is diagnosed are delusions or false beliefs, hallucinations and thought disorder. The delusions may be paranoid or persecutory and the person becoming ill may believe everyone is against them when this is far from the truth, or they may have thoughts that they are very powerful, grandiose and important. Hallucinations are very difficult to explain to anyone. People may see things which are not there (visual hallucinations), or hear voices when no one else is there (auditory hallucinations). These voices are really the patient's thoughts, somehow magnified, so that they seem to be speaking out loud. The thoughts may often be of a very unpleasant nature telling the patient to do all sorts of things quite against his or her nature. Thought disorder is self-explanatory. Thought may become jumbled and so may speech. Sometimes the mind may become a total blank, with no thoughts whatsoever. To a person becoming mentally ill these are fearful and frightening changes in personality. If you can put yourself in such a person's shoes you can begin to feel a lot of compassion and sympathy for them. You must learn not to take offence by things said by someone becoming mentally ill. In this way, by not reacting adversely, you can become a stabilising effect on the ill person. 'Judge Not' is a very important precept.

Importance of recognising symptoms

At first, when a person is becoming mentally ill, he may not be abnormal at all for much of the time. Unhappily his well friends will remember how horrid he has been to them when he was showing symptoms. They may feel resentment if they have not learned about mental illness. It is possible that the ill person, when feeling well, will scarcely remember his ill behaviour. To him it may be as a dream. It is important to remember this. Schizophrenia is a disease which often attacks the adolescent or young adult, with boys having an earlier onset usually than girls and also, very often, a more severe illness, but the illness can start at any age from childhood to old age. It is really important for everyone to be able to recognise the symptoms. If you were so unfortunate as to be developing such an illness, a recognition of the symptoms depends, at least in part, in your having learned these symptoms. If they are firmly in your mind you might remember them and if you become ill, you can get treatment then as soon as possible.

The nature of illness

Schizophrenia is most probably not one illness but an umbrella term covering a number of different diseases, each having its own cause, but sharing the same psychiatric symptoms. There is a genetic component (i.e. there is a hereditary aspect) to at least some of these diseases. The causes may be anywhere in the body or brain and only gradually and intermittently affect the brain. On the other hand diseases of the brain, like a brain tumour or an infection like meningitis, can also upset the working of the brain. It seems likely, from a great deal of evidence, that the origin of much psychiatric disease arises in the body. Many bodily diseases are known to give rise to psychiatric symptoms which, if untreated, can have profound effects on the brain. An American physician, the late Dr F. Curtis Dohan, produced evidence supporting his hypothesis that the eating of grains and sometimes the drinking of milk, over a long period, in someone who was genetically vulnerable to schizophrenia, eventually produced the psychiatric symptoms. Dohan thought schizophrenia was closely related to a disease of known sensitivity to grains – coeliac disease. Dohan said that in schizophrenia, wheat, rye, oats, barley, sorghum and millet in descending order of toxicity could eventually cause psychiatric symptoms. There may often be blood sugar problems in schizophrenia which affect the glucose supply to the brain. Infections also may be particularly severe, particularly viral infections, such as influenza, measles and glandular fever and these infections bring on schizophrenia in someone genetically vulnerable. The hopeful aspect of all these other diseases, which may be the cause of the psychiatric symptoms, is that, for the most part, if looked for and found, they are treatable. In these cases schizophrenia can be a curable disease.

Alcohol and street drugs

Alcohol and street drugs are very bad for those with incipient schizophrenia. They can worsen the illness and confuse the diagnosis. It is totally essential for the well-being of future generations that the present generation shuns both alcohol and street drugs. They are extraordinarily harmful to all and destructive of happiness to those who take them. To those becoming mentally ill they are especially harmful. At first they may seem to reduce the alarming symptoms but this is only a temporary and false brightening. If you are mentally well you want to stay that way. If you are mentally ill, or potentially so, run a mile away from such temptations as alcohol and drugs.

Smoking

Many people with schizophrenia are exceedingly heavy smokers and their addiction makes them feel better for a very short period of time. It is much better not to smoke as smoking rapidly becomes an addiction in those becoming mentally ill and can lead to severe circulatory problems.

Food

We all need to feed our brains to derive the best we can from them. Fresh fruit and vegetables, especially raw or lightly cooked, are nourishing. Fish is an excellent food, specially fatty fish, like salmon and mackerel, but all fish is good unless you are allergic to it. Turkey, chicken and other birds are also excellent foods. It may be that for those who come from mentally unstable families a reduction in the consumption of wheat, milk and sugar is helpful. Glucose and fructose (fruit sugar) may be better sugars to take.

Symptoms to look out for What should we do?

We know very little really about schizophrenia but try to remember the symptoms to help your friends or yourself if you find yourself losing mental stability. The sooner treatment starts, the better the response to it and the less likely is the disease to become severe. Remember too, that usually, perhaps always, there are physical symptoms that may occur before the development of the psychiatric symptoms. The patient-to-be may lose a great deal of weight. Their face may be thin and very pale. Their pupils in their eyes may be large or very tiny. The patient may have digestive problems, constipation or vomiting. Some may become anorexic, particularly perhaps young women. A flu-like condition may develop with a slight rise in temperature. There may be a great lack of energy in the day and overactivity at night. There may be palpitations of the heart and panic accompanying them. Such panic is overwhelming and produces great fear. Anger and violence may accompany the fear. This is quite out of the control of the patient. All our emotions are chemically caused. For the most part we are the product of our biochemical make-up. We cannot choose if we are nice or nasty, good-tempered or bad-tempered. We can learn though how to restore our personality to what it was before becoming mentally ill.

Medical illness which could be the cause of the mental symptoms must be very thoroughly looked for by the doctors and, if found, treated. Apparently vascular disease, gut disease, diabetes and other endocrine (hormonal) diseases are particularly

---

Schizophrenia is most probably not one illness but an umbrella term covering a number of different diseases, each having its own cause

---

common. One American writer, Shiffler, said 'There are no psychiatric patients, only medical patients with varying degrees of psychopathology' (psychiatric mental symptoms).

Eat well. Practise yoga and meditation. If the autonomic nervous system is involved in the disease this may help. See you take enough vitamins and minerals especially B12 and folic acid (taken at the same time always) and magnesium which may be especially helpful if there are heart symptoms. Any magnesium salt will do. There are many different ones in Health Food Shops. If you have not one near you Milk of Magnesia can be taken in the short term. If you have a kidney condition do not take magnesium.

Specific information regarding nutritional supplements can be obtained from the Schizophrenia Association of Great Britain including details of the most important fish oils. These supplements are available from the assocsiation.

Summary

This is but a brief report of the sort of disease schizophrenia is. Our umbrella logo signifies not one disease but many sheltering under the name. Remember, in many of its manifestations it can be curable, or, if not curable, treatable with minimal doses of medication and diet, if appropriate, and increased vitamins and minerals as described in the SAGB's Management Notes.

Do not take it out on your family and friends. Do all you can to get well. Do not despair and help one another, accepting always the physical basis of personality which is true for all of us and bear in mind that personality can change very slowly often because of the onset of disease affecting the brain. You are not bad if your behaviour alters through disease, but ill.

What do I do if I feel worried about something or I need explanation, advice or help? Do not put off doing something. Go to see your doctor or talk to your student welfare officer, personal tutor or family.

Mental health and the media

An introductory resource for students

Mental health and the media – the case for change

'Madness has always had the power to frighten and fascinate a fact exploited by some journalists. It means that people with mental health problems have been portrayed as violent and dangerous.'[1]

Emotive terms like 'psycho', 'nutter' or 'lunatic' are used by journalists on a daily basis in reporting on mental health issues. The use of such words is rarely questioned in the media, particularly when they are such an easy way to grab readers' attention. However, this practice feeds the public's ignorance and fear of people who have mental health problems, rather than encouraging respect and understanding. Despite the impression given by the media the fact is the vast majority of people with mental health problems are not violent. To suggest otherwise at a time when psychiatric hospitals are being closed and care in the community is being developed should concern us all: 'Because we live in an increasingly stressful world, where people experiencing mental health problems form a significant proportion of society, it is no longer tenable to ignore or consign mental distress to the margins.'[2]

How does the media affect the public's beliefs about mental health?

'Hungerford, that type of thing – anything you see on the news, it's likely to be violent when it is connected with mentally ill people.'[3]

The media plays a powerful part in forming people's attitudes about the society in which they live. Stories about people with mental health problems, and associated issues like care in the community, are rarely out of the headlines – and none more so than news stories linking mental health and violence.

A study by the Glasgow University Media Group based on audience research confirmed the belief that people who saw a strong link between mental health and violence largely derived their beliefs from the media. Thankfully though the media is not the only influence on people's attitudes. The study also found that people who had first-hand experience of mental health issues through their family and friends, were much more critical of the media and more open to alternative ways of looking at the issue.

'I keep an open mind and I don't believe everything I read. I work with people and I hear what they say but I think they don't really know until they've experienced it.'[4]

A glaring problem with the media's portrayal of mental health and violence is that it is at odds with the facts. While the number of homicides has more than doubled over the last 40 years, in comparison those homicides committed by people with mental health problems have remained steady over that time. When violence does occur in the vast majority of cases it is against friends and family, or through suicide, but rarely towards strangers as news reports tend to suggest. As the Royal College of Psychiatrists' *Report of the Confidential Inquiry into Homicides by Mental Ill People* found: 'Random killing of a stranger by a psychotic individual is a rare occurrence . . . people with schizophrenia were one hundred times more likely to kill themselves than others.'

How does the media affect the situation of people with mental health problems?

'People think it is a weakness to have a mental illness. But anyone, given certain circumstances can have a breakdown. It's something we all recognise and because we recognise it in ourselves, we reject it in others.' (Philip, diagnosed with manic depression)

The media's linking of mental health and violence has very damaging effects for people with mental health problems living in the community. It means people are often too frightened to seek help because of the stigma that surrounds mental health. Even those who do find help face fear and hostility from their own family and friends because of media-fed prejudices about mental health problems.

'The mentally ill are generally portrayed as violent psychopaths and the lack of basic understanding in the general public causes the fear to be multiplied.'[5]

Prejudice about mental health problems surfaces in all sectors of the media, from television to local newspapers. It crops up in tabloid

language like 'insane' or 'nutter' and in the unquestioning use of medical-based vocabulary with words like 'sufferer'. Though the editors of 'quality' newspapers like the *Times* or *Guardian* would decry such crude tabloid language, their newspapers more subtle practice of placing front-page stories about violence next to calls for changes in mental health policy, is based on the same assumptions about mental health and violence as the more obviously tabloid approach. Without thinking through these issues, attempts at sympathetic reporting can easily end up as prejudiced and patronising.

Journalists can also create problems by failing to think carefully about the common diagnoses given to people with mental health problems. For example schizophrenia has nothing to do with split personality. Rather it is used by the medical profession to describe a state in which a person cannot distinguish between the real and the imaginary. Similarly manic depression does not as is commonly understood involve daily mood swings, but rather movements from depression to elation over many weeks or months.

Much of the pressure for more informed reporting has come from people with mental health problems. They are challenging both the way the mental health system treats people, and the way the media depicts them as 'mad, bad and dangerous'. This 'user' (as in user of mental health services) or 'survivor' (as in survivor of the psychiatric system) movement is already well developed in the US and the Netherlands, and is well developed in this country. Gradually the media is starting to realise that people who have had mental health problems have some powerful stories to tell.

How can media reporting on mental health be challenged?

The simplest way to complain about reports on mental health is to write direct to the editor of a publication or programme concerned. When this fails there are a number of formal complaints bodies which adjudicate on issues like accuracy and prejudice. However, as in the case of the Press Complaints Commission

(PCC) for example, which oversees the newspaper industry, in reality this is far from straightforward. While there are two clauses particularly relevant to mental health in the PCC's code of practice, one on accuracy and another on discrimination, in its adjudications over complaints it rarely comes down against newspapers despite the amount of bigoted reporting that goes on. It was only this year the PCC made its first ruling against a national tabloid on the grounds that it was prejudiced about someone with mental health problems after describing him as a 'raving nutter'.

Projects like Headlines, based at Mental Health Media (MHM), work with people with mental health problems to challenge inaccurate and damaging reporting at a local and national newspaper level. The work also involves showing user groups

ways of obtaining more positive reporting in their locality, through building relationships with journalists and attracting publicity. At a national level this involves trying to gain more positive coverage through events like World Mental Health Day in mid-October and MHMs awards held at the same time.

References
1   Headlines leaflet
2   Mental Health in the Media, a good practice guide for journalists and broadcasters; the Scottish Association for Mental Health
3   Mass Media Representations of Mental Health/Illness, Report for the Health Education Board for Scotland; Glasgow University Media Group
4   Ibid.
5   Ibid.
© *Mental Health Media (MHM)*

Key national findings

Counting the Cost

- 73% of all respondents felt the media coverage of mental health issues over the last three years had been unfair, unbalanced or very negative. Only 12% of all respondents felt it had been fair, balanced or very positive.
- 50% of all respondents said that this media coverage had a negative effect on their mental health. 34% of all respondents felt more anxious or depressed, 22% felt more withdrawn and isolated, 8% felt more suicidal, 11% needed additional support from mental health services whilst 13% felt reluctant to contact these services for support.
- Only 14% of all respondents said that this media coverage had a positive effect on their mental health.
- 24% of all respondents had experienced hostility from their neighbours and local communities as a result of media reports.
- 33% of all respondents said media coverage had put them off applying for jobs or volunteering.
- A significant number of respondents did mention how helpful some programmes and articles had been in helping to educate other people, and sometimes enabling them to gain more insight into their own mental health problems.
- Respondents were asked to analyse the way different media had covered mental health stories. Key findings were that:
- Regional newspapers, regional TV news and regional radio news programmes were all felt to be fairer or more mixed in their coverage of mental health issues than the national media.
- Overall, radio news programmes ranked the fairest news media, followed by TV news and then newspapers.
- Magazines ranked the fairest of all non-news media (51%), followed by TV soaps (36%), TV chat shows (33%) and then TV drama series (30%).

© 2000 Mind (National Association for Mental Health)

Working on the verge of a breakdown

Mental illness is one of the last taboos, even though it afflicts one in four

By Hilary Freeman

Four years ago, Steve (not his real name), 29, a press officer, spent three months in hospital. None of his colleagues came to visit him and when he was discharged he had to start looking for a new job.

Today, Steve doesn't mention his time off sick. He claims he spent those three months 'travelling'. He won't apply for jobs that require a medical examination and he won't join his company's private medical insurance scheme.

Steve had a breakdown. Always prone to depression, he was unable to cope with the combined stresses of moving to London, a new job, long hours and an unsympathetic boss. He swallowed a bottle of pills and was found just in time by a concerned friend.

Steve still takes antidepressants and mood-stabilising drugs and is prone to anxiety attacks when work pressure builds up. You'd never know it to look at him: he's charming, intelligent and successful – in fact, he's just been given a promotion. But he's terrified that if his boss finds out about his 'guilty secret' he will be dismissed on the spot.

'It's ironic,' he says. 'I'm openly gay and yet I won't reveal that I have a common health problem. I just can't face the stigma.'

Mental health problems are the last great taboo. It's no surprise: the media perpetuates the myth that mentally ill people are dangerous. The truth is rather different. An official 1997 government study showed that you are 400 times more likely to die from the flu than to be killed by a mentally ill person.

And mental health charity, Mind, estimates that in any one year one in four people will have some kind of mental illness. The most common, mixed anxiety and depression, affects 7.7% of the population. Every year, more than 100,000 people attempt suicide in this country.

Not to mention that the kind of life changes experienced by young professionals – like moving away from home and starting a new job – are triggers for mental health problems.

The point is that either you, someone you know, or someone you work with is likely to have experienced a mental health problem at some time. Strange that no one talks openly about it. Or is it?

Take this case study from Mind's files: 'On two occasions I lied when I applied for jobs. On both these occasions I said that my absence from employment was due to a term spent in prison. I was accepted for the first and short-listed for the second. Whenever I have been truthful about my psychiatric past, I have never been accepted for a job.'

That's why people like Karen (not her real name), 25, hide their illness. A marketing graduate, Karen suffered from severe anorexia throughout her teenage years. 'I don't think you ever completely recover,' she says. 'When I started work I was petrified at the prospect of business lunches, or drinks with my colleagues. I did anything to avoid them. At the medical for my current job I had to tell the nurse. I couldn't believe the panic on her face.'

> **MIND has drawn up a checklist of adjustments employers can make to remove the barriers faced by people with mental health problems at work**

Although the Disability Discrimination Act covers mental health problems, it is difficult to enforce because unlike physical disability, mental illness is by nature invisible.

MIND has drawn up a checklist of adjustments employers can make to remove the barriers faced by people with mental health problems at work. They include flexi-hours, re-organisation of work duties and a period of readjustment after illness.

If you have a mental health problem, there are no easy answers. Terry Dray, Agcas equal opportunities co-ordinator, admits that the stigma of mental illness makes applying for jobs difficult: 'You could pre-empt awkward questions by obtaining a medical reference from the Employment Medical Advisory Service. This explains your condition and your suitability for work.

'It's also a good idea to target disability-friendly employers. You'll be able to get a list of these in your university careers office.'

Is honesty always the best policy? Mike Emmott, adviser, employee relations at the IPD, says he'd never encourage anyone to lie on their application form, but he understands why people do. 'Unless your mental health problem is directly relevant to your job or it will affect your performance, you're not legally obliged to say everything about your medical history,' he says.

'The most important thing is not to let your illness scar you for life by destroying your self-confidence. If you believe you're stigmatised and will never get a job, you'll become a self-fulfilling prophecy.'

• Want to know more? Mind Information Line: 0345 660 163; Samaritans (24-hour helpline): 0345 909 090; Depression Alliance (answerphone): 020 7633 9929; Saneline: 0345 678 000

Depression

Information from the Royal College of Psychiatrists

Introduction

Depression is a very common experience. Everyone feels fed up, miserable or sad sometimes. Usually, the reason seems obvious – a disappointment, frustration, losing something or someone important – but not always; sometimes we're just 'in a mood', 'have got the hump', 'feel blue', 'got out of bed the wrong side', and we really don't know why.

Depression can be so severe that life hardly feels worth living and sufferers often find that they just cannot cope with things as they used to. Other people may think they have 'given in', but depression of this degree is an illness and needs treatment. It is not a sign of weakness – even powerful personalities can experience deep depression. Winston Churchill called it his 'black dog'.

As in the everyday depression that we all experience from time to time, there will sometimes be an obvious reason for becoming depressed, sometimes not. Physical illnesses, bereavement, money and housing worries or relationship problems may all bring about a period of depression. Unlike the short episodes of depression that most of us experience, with depressive illness the feeling of depression is much more intense and goes on for much longer – months rather than days or weeks.

Seeking help

When feelings of depression are worse than usual and don't seem to get any better we may need to seek help. We may also find that depression affects our work, our interests and our feelings towards family and friends. If we find ourselves feeling that life is not worth living, or that other people would be better off without us, we should seek help without delay. It may be enough to talk things over with a relative or friend, who may be able to help us through a bad patch in our life. If this doesn't seem to help, it will probably be time to visit our family doctor.

We may not realise how depressed we are if the depression has come on slowly, or we blame ourselves for being lazy or feeble. Other people may have to point this out to us and some of us need persuading that seeking help is not a sign of weakness! We may try to cope with our feelings of depression by being very busy, making ourselves even more stressed and exhausted. Sometimes depression may not show itself as feelings of unhappiness, but may produce bodily pain, headaches or sleeplessness.

Of course, we may not actually realise how depressed we are, because it has come on so gradually, or because we blame ourselves for being lazy or feeble. We are determined to struggle on, and may need to be persuaded by others that it is not a sign of weakness to seek help. Or we may try to make up for or escape from our real feelings by rushing around and being overactive – and then wonder why we feel so stressed and exhausted. Sometimes our disturbed feelings may not show themselves as unhappiness, which we might easily recognise, but in some physical form such as constant headaches, pain of one kind or another or difficulty in staying asleep.

Symptoms

Certain symptoms can help you, your family or your doctor decide that you are suffering from depression:

- feelings of unhappiness that don't go away
- losing interest in life
- becoming unable to enjoy anything
- finding it hard to make even simple decisions
- feeling utterly tired
- feeling restless and agitated
- losing appetite and weight (some people find they do the reverse and put on weight)
- difficulty in sleeping
- waking up earlier than usual

- going off 'sex'
- losing self-confidence
- feeling useless, inadequate and hopeless
- avoiding other people
- feeling irritable
- feeling worse at a particular time of day, usually mornings
- thinking of suicide – this is very common in depression and is much better talked about than ignored

Causes

Friends and relatives as well as the depressed person are anxious to know why they should be depressed. Usually there is more than one reason, and these differ from one person to another.

It is quite normal to feel depressed after a distressing event, but normally after a time we 'work through' our feelings about what has happened, and come to terms with them. But sometimes such events lead to more serious and persistent depression from which we find it harder to emerge.

Circumstances at the time we are stressed play a part. If we are alone, have no friends around, have other worries or are physically run down, then we may become more seriously depressed where in happier times we would cope.

Depression often strikes when we are physically ill. This is true for life-threatening illnesses like cancer and heart disease, but also for illnesses that are long and uncomfortable or painful, like arthritis or bronchitis. Younger people may become depressed after viral infections, like 'flu'.

Personality may also play a part in depression. Although anyone can become depressed under certain circumstances, some of us seem to be more vulnerable than others. This may be because of the particular make-up of our body, because of experiences early in our life, or both.

It seems that women get depressed more than men. This is probably because men are less likely to admit their feelings, and more likely to bottle them up or express them in aggression or through drinking heavily. Women can be under more stress, say from having to work and at the same time look after a child.

About one in ten people who suffer from serious depression will also have periods when they are elated and overactive. This form of depression, known as manic depression, affects the same number of men and women and tends to run in families.

Treatment

Most people with depression are treated by their family doctor. Depending on your symptoms, the severity of the depression and the circumstances, the doctor may suggest some form of talking treatment, antidepressant tablets, or both.

Talking: simply talking about your feelings may be helpful, however depressed you are. But exploring and confronting the reasons behind your depression takes energy and motivation – this may not be possible if your depression is severe.

If the depression seems connected with a special problem such as your relationship with your partner, then a specialised agency, such as Relate, may be most helpful in enabling you to sort out your feelings. If it seems about suffering from disability or caring for a relative, then sharing experiences with others in a self-help group may provide just the support you need.

Sometimes it is hard to express your real feelings even to close friends.

Talking things through with a trained counsellor or therapist can bring tremendous relief. Just having another person's undivided attention is likely to make you feel better about yourself.

If your depression is caused by not getting over the death of someone close to you, talking is especially effective.

Antidepressants: if your depression is severe or goes on for a long time, your doctor may suggest that you take a course of antidepressants.

These are not tranquillisers, although they may help you to feel less anxious and agitated. They are not addictive. However, they do help people with depression to feel and cope better, so that they can start to enjoy life and deal with their problems effectively again.

It is important to remember that, unlike many medicines you won't feel the effect of antidepressants straight away. People often don't notice any improvement in their mood for 2 or 3 weeks, although some of the other problems may improve more quickly. For instance, people often notice that they are sleeping better and feeling less anxious in the first few days.

Like all medicines, antidepressants do have some side-effects, though these are usually mild and tend to wear off as the treatment goes on. A dry mouth and constipation are quite common: at least they indicate that the tablets are working, and your doctor is likely to tell you to carry on with them.

Different antidepressants have different effects. Your doctor can advise you what to expect, and will want to know if you experience anything which worries you. 'Will the tablets make me drowsy?' is an important question.

Generally they are taken at night, so any drowsiness can then help you to sleep. However, if you feel sleepy during the day you should not drive or work with machinery till the effect wears off.

You can eat a normal diet while taking most of these tablets (if not, your doctor will tell you) and they are compatible with pain-killers, antibiotics and the Pill. You should avoid alcohol, though. If taken with the tablets, it can make you very sleepy.

Not getting better

A small number of depressed people do not get better with these treatments.

These people are likely to be referred to a psychiatrist for more specialised help. A psychiatrist is a medical doctor who specialises in the treatment of emotional and mental disorders. The first interview with a psychiatrist will probably last about an hour, and you may be invited to bring a relative or friend with you if you wish. There is no need to feel nervous; the sort of questions asked are likely to be practical rather than deeply probing. The psychiatrist will want to find out about your general background and about any serious illnesses or emotional problems you may have had in the past. He or she will ask about what has been happening in your life recently, how the depression has developed and whether you have had any treatment for it already. It can sometimes be difficult to answer all these questions, but they help the doctor to get to know you as a person and decide on what would be the best treatment for you. This might be different tablets or talking treatment, perhaps involving members of your family. If your depression is severe or needs a specialised type of treatment, it might be necessary to come into hospital, although this is only necessary in about one in every 100 people with depression.

ECT (Electro-convulsive therapy)

Most people don't like the idea of ECT. However, it is a very effective treatment for very severe depression and works more quickly than tablets.

Most people who suffer from depression never need it.

ECT is usually given in hospital but can be given to out-patients. Firstly, a light anaesthetic is given. While the person is asleep, a muscle-relaxing drug is given followed by a brief electrical current which passes through the brain for a fraction of a second. It is always given under strict medical supervision. It all takes about 15 minutes and all you will be aware of is having gone to sleep. Afterwards people sometimes have a headache or a short period of feeling muddled, but these usually pass off quickly. There is absolutely no evidence that properly-given ECT harms the brain in any way. It is the most effective treatment in severe depression, as many people who have had it will testify.

How to help yourself

Even when a doctor is involved in the treatment of depression, there are things you can do to help yourself:

1. Don't bottle things up: if you've recently had some bad news, or a major upset in your life, try to tell people close to you about it and how it feels. It helps to relive the painful experience several times, to have a good cry, and talk things through. This is part of the mind's natural healing mechanism.

2. Do something: get out of doors for some exercise, even if only for a long walk. This will help you to keep physically fit, and you may sleep better.

    While you may not feel able to work, it is always good to try to keep up some activity – house-work, do-it-yourself (even changing a light bulb) or part of your normal routine. This will help take your mind off those painful feelings which only make you more depressed when allowed to sweep over you. You may also feel a little less helpless.

3. Eat a good, balanced diet, even though you may not feel like eating. Fresh fruit and vegetables are especially recommended. People with severe depression can lose weight and run low in vitamins, which only makes matters worse.

4. Resist the temptation to drown your sorrows. Alcohol actually makes depression worse. It may make you feel better for a few hours, but will then make you feel worse then ever. Too much alcohol stops you from seeking the right help and from solving problems; it is also bad for your bodily health.

5. Try not to worry about finding it difficult to sleep. Even if you're not actually asleep, it can still be helpful to listen to the radio or watch TV while you're resting your body. If you can

occupy your mind in this way, you may find that you feel less anxious and are able to drop off to sleep.

6. Remind yourself that you are suffering from depression – something which many other people have gone through – and that you will eventually come out of it, as they did, even though it does not feel like it at the time. Depression can even be a useful experience, in that some people emerge stronger and better able to cope than before. Situations and relationships may be seen more clearly, and you may now have the strength and wisdom to make important decisions and changes in your life which you were avoiding before.

Relatives and friends

Family and friends often want to know what they can do to help. Being a good listener (and a patient listener if you've heard it all before) is very important.

It is helpful to spend time with someone who is depressed. They don't need to be nagged, but they need to be encouraged, perhaps to talk, but also to keep going with some of the things they normally do. Someone who is depressed will find it hard to believe that they can ever get better.

Reassurance that they will get better can be helpful, but may have to be given over and over again. On a practical level, make sure that they are eating enough and help them to stay away from alcohol.

If the depressed person is getting worse and has started to talk of not wanting to live or even hinting at harming themselves, take these statements seriously and insist that their doctor is informed. Try to help the person to accept the treatment and don't say 'I wouldn't take the tablets if I were you' or 'You don't want to go to a psychiatrist – you're not mad!' If you have doubts about the treatment, discuss them first with the doctor.

• The above information is from the Royal College of Psychiatrists. See page 41 for their address details.
© Royal College of Psychiatrists

Coping with depression

Information from Depression Alliance

Self-help

Self-help starts with learning more about depression and discovering ways of coping. This can be done on an individual basis and through contact with other people to share experiences. Helping yourself to understand depression and to find ways of managing it can reduce the feelings of helplessness and hopelessness that often arise.

Self-help is complementary to professional treatment and should not be seen as an alternative.

A valuable step forward in helping yourself get out of depression may be to join a self-help group, if there is one close to your home.

Self-help groups

The core of Depression Alliance is our network of self-help groups. At these informal groups, people receive encouragement, reassurance, support and a 'listening ear'. They can share their experiences, and also information and ways of coping. They can discuss their feelings, without guilt, in a sympathetic environment. Group meetings are not places where people just listen to each other's problems. Gatherings are usually lively and positive occasions. Groups do not offer therapy, but being part of a group may be therapeutic. Offering support to others can raise your self-esteem. People may share concerns and difficulties about treatments, medication or services but they are supported in collaborating fully with the relevant professionals.

People with depression can try any of the ways of coping which feel appropriate to them. Many people have found their depression eased by a combination of the following:

Gathering information

There is a wide range of materials, books, videos, cassettes, articles, TV and radio programmes etc., giving practical advice for people with depression and their carers. A better

understanding of depression, its possible causes, treatments and ways of coping can reduce fear, guilt, misconceptions and stigma.

Relaxation

Depression frequently causes tension and anxiety which can affect many aspects of life. People may become ultra-sensitive and irritable. There are many ways to relax – exercise, cassette tapes, yoga, meditation, aromatherapy, massage etc. can all be effective in reducing anxiety and tension. One organisation which offers advice on relaxation and stress relief is The Stress Management Training Institute.

Exercise

Many people who are depressed may become exhausted and totally lacking in motivation. If you can manage some form of exercise, however gentle, it will help you feel better and more positive. It seems to be even more effective if taken in fresh air.

A change of lifestyle

Some people who have depression are perfectionists who drive themselves too hard. Impossible standards may need to be lowered, and workloads reduced, so that life can be lived at a slower pace. These changes do not make us less valuable people, but put us in command of our life, rather than being a member of the 'rat race'.

Breaks

Holidays or short breaks bring relief by breaking up the routine which so easily lets us get into a rut.

Diet

Under- or overeating can be symptoms of depression, and it can be easy to eat junk food. If we miss out valuable nutrients we are more likely to feel tired and run down, so try to eat regularly and well. Try to include some fresh vegetables and fruit in your meals.

Interests

It can help to occupy your mind with absorbing subjects, interests or hobbies. Studying, watching a special TV programme or film or listening to music can be difficult as concentration is often impaired, but this can be improved with practice.

Things to avoid

Props such as smoking, non-prescribed drugs and alcohol can be damaging. In particular, alcohol is a depressant and despite giving us a temporary 'lift' can make matters worse as we try to retain the 'lift' by drinking more and more.

© Depression Alliance

Why did my world have to change?

Some support for teenagers whose parents have manic depression

'I was totally confused about what was happening'

When a parent goes into a manic attack for the first time, family life becomes like a weird bad dream. You may recognise some signs, like the person being 'high' – excited, talking all the time (and not making sense), hardly needing any sleep. Sometimes they say nasty things or have sudden rages which are frightening. They may go on a spending spree, start buying everyone big presents or things for the house. At the same time ordinary life grinds to a halt, the house is a mess which they don't notice, no one cooks a proper meal or does the ironing. The first thing to understand is that manic depression is an illness. Your Mum or Dad cannot help being ill. Lots of people (one in 100) get this illness. They need the care of doctors, and there is medical treatment which will help.

'She made me so embarrassed'

All teenagers cringe at their parents' behaviour occasionally, but a person who has manic depression can really drop you in it – in front of strangers at the supermarket, or in the street, or with your friends – grabbing hold of them, gabbling wild theories and plans. Soon you stop inviting people home. The illness becomes a secret, which you are ashamed of. You want to stay loyal to your family, you may wonder if it's your fault, and you may be very angry.

Once the illness is diagnosed, you will find there are people who will understand these painful mixed-up feelings.

'I hated seeing my Dad in hospital'

Psychiatric hospitals can be frightening places because people there are often very sad or disturbed. Ask to see Mum/Dad in private. Talk to medical staff; plan ahead what questions you need to ask. One topic to understand is medication, which will calm down a person who is manic, or lift them if they have become depressed. It can take time to find the right level of medication. Once this has been established, and the person sticks to it regularly, the tablets can help control the illness.

'I just couldn't get my homework done on time'

Rushing in late to school, no breakfast, miserable, homework not done – no wonder your schoolwork has gone downhill for the moment. There is no need for everyone in the world to know, but your school should be told what has happened.

Some teachers can be surprisingly understanding. At times school can offer a refuge from problems at home. It would also be good to confide in one or two friends, they may really want to listen and help you.

'I had to look after my Mum instead of her looking after me'

You may have to look after Mum/Dad, get them meals, remind them to take their tablets, do shopping, even perhaps look after younger brothers and sisters. This situation will not last for ever, just do the best you can. It does not matter if the house is not brilliant and meals are quick and easy. If Mum/Dad has been overspending, that is not your problem.

Perhaps your other parent, the one who is well, does not live with you, or if they do, is so distressed or preoccupied because of the situation that they have not noticed how upset you are. You are still entitled to ask them to give you their attention, comfort, explanations. Some people find they eventually draw closer as a result.

Survival tactics

A person who is 'high' can be very irritating to live with. It is natural for you to cherish your room and your privacy, and unfortunately they may have lost the perception to respect this, coming into your room at all hours and using your things. Don't argue with them when they are like this. Be tactful and tolerant of what they are doing, but look for somewhere to let off steam elsewhere.

It's better to avoid confrontation when a person is manic, leave the room or go for a walk if they pick an argument. There is always the library to do homework, spend time at a friend's house if you can.

'Who will help me?'

What about you? You were just finding out who you were, wanting to be your own person with your own rights, opinions and feelings, now this crisis has hit you.

It will help you to talk to an adult you can trust – a family friend, relative, or teacher, someone at church, or youth group; if there isn't an obvious person, ask your teacher or GP, and they might recommend someone.

It's been proved many times over that people recover better from difficult situations if they come out with their feelings, not just hide them or try to pretend they don't exist.

One day you might want to have counselling or meet other people like you, with parents who suffer from manic depression. Listening to them, telling what happened to your family, finding you are not alone with this problem, can make it seem a great deal more bearable.

'Dad threatened to kill himself'

There is no single pattern to manic depression, as people vary in how the illness affects them, but very often after the manic, or high phase, there is a downer – really persistent depression that your Mum/Dad will not be able to quickly shake themselves out of. Drug medication will help their mood to lift, but they may stay in bed, cry, not look after themselves. Tell your GP if they are threatening suicide.

Be prepared to tell the depressed person, over and over again, things will get better. Give yourself a break like going round to a friend's house to watch TV – or write a poem, paint a picture – that can be a great release.

'It was great when Mum was better'
After being high or very depressed, many people with manic depression remain well for years. But if your parent suffers another attack in the future, now that you have learnt something about this illness you will be better equipped to cope.

If you can be positive, you will be helping yourself and your whole family.

Give Mum/Dad your support, showing patience and understanding even when things are difficult. Like you, they need space and their own

place in the house to relax. Encourage them to look after their appearance, tell them a joke or two. Remind them that you care for them, and that they will recover soon.

They may have been ill, but they never stopped loving you, and still want the very best for you. With time and help, the future is still there for you. © *Manic Depression Fellowship*

SANELINE

Help at the end of the line

S ANELINE is committed to providing accurate and up-to-date information to give callers options for action and to encourage them to benefit from whatever network of care exists in their own area. It also offers emotional and crisis support to people suffering from mental illness, their families and friends and information to professionals and organisations working in the mental health field.

What is SANELINE?

SANELINE is the only national, out-of-hours, telephone helpline for anyone coping with mental illness in the UK. SANELINE was initially set up in London in 1992 and now has two 'satellites' in Macclesfield and Bristol. The helpline is staffed by volunteers, who have access to SANELINE's unique computer database, and the lines are open from 2pm until midnight every day of the year, including Christmas.

The SANELINE volunteer

SANELINE is staffed by volunteers who are ordinary members of the public and do not need any specific educational qualifications. They are required to be non-judgmental, have empathy with those affected by mental illness and be willing to work one 4-hour shift per week on the helpline – and be prepared to go through SANELINE's thorough initial training and probation and subsequently to attend an ongoing training programme.

The volunteers are carefully selected and given 40 hours' initial training over a period of six weeks. During that training they learn about mental health issues from leading professionals in the mental health field as well as from sufferers and carers. The volunteers are also trained to listen sympathetically, to discover the needs of the caller, and to use the SANELINE database which contains over 13,000 records of services throughout the United Kingdom.

These records, provided by medical professionals, legal experts, local Health Authorities, Social Services and voluntary organisations, are continually updated by SANELINE staff.

Volunteers are able to help by:
- offering support and reassurance during periods of crisis
- helping callers to consider options for action
- giving information from the database on local services, including telephone numbers, addresses, opening hours, guidance on access etc.
- discussing symptoms of illnesses, and treatments available from medication to psychotherapy and counselling
- offering to provide ongoing support for people in a crisis situation who may benefit from SANELINE's Caller Care Service
- SANELINE can be contacted by calling 0345 67 8000.

© *SANE*

Talking therapies

Information from the Robert Mond Memorial Trust (RMMT)

Over the years, traditional psychoanalysis has been shown in clinical studies to be ineffective in the treatment of depression and anxiety disorders. In the world of psychiatry, the theories of Freud, Adler and Jung are now largely regarded as historically interesting but therapeutically ineffective.

However the role of what is now referred to as 'talking therapies' has taken increased prominence, and two forms of treatments, Cognitive Behavioural Therapy (CBT) and Interpersonal Therapy (ITP) have gained prominence. They have been subject to rigorous clinical testing, especially in the USA, and have been found to be as effective as antidepressants in many areas of depression.

Both these therapeutic modes are essentially pragmatic. Aaron Beck, one of the influential pioneers of cognitive therapy, proposed the view that most disturbances arise from faulty cognitions, and/or faulty cognitive processing. He therefore proposed that the remedy for this was to be found in correcting these faulty cognitions, and therapy concentrates on present problems and present thinking, in sharp distinction from psychotherapy which concentrates on past historical events. The difference between CBT and analysis can be simply put in that while analysis sees the problem to be the reflection of some deeper cause (often in the subconscious), CBT, however, sees the problem to be the cause itself. Remove the problem thought and there is no unconscious route – the problem has been eradicated.

There is still debate as to exactly how effective CBT and ITP are in severe cases of depression, but there is no doubt as to the effective role of talking therapies either alone or in conjunction with antidepressant therapy. It is very unfortunate that there are few cognitive analysts and fewer who are trained in interpersonal therapy. We hope that more people will see this as a rewarding career and will seek qualification as a therapist.

Even if you do not have access to a cognitive therapist, remember that talking helps. Find a friend who will listen to what you say and offer practical advice. Try to dispel negative emotions and think of positive things that you can do each day that will bring you enjoyment and pleasure. Depression is not an excuse to beat oneself up psychologically! Getting better is often getting back self-esteem.

Selected sources:
Science and Practice of Cognitive Behaviour Therapy – edited by David M. Clark and Christopher G. Fairburn.
© *Robert Mond Memorial Trust (RMMT)*

Understanding and respecting the person with dementia

Information from the Alzheimer's Disease Society

If you are caring for someone with dementia you will want to ensure that they are always treated with respect and dignity and as an individual person, however little they may seem to understand.

Someone with dementia, whose mental abilities are declining, will feel vulnerable and in need of reassurance and support. It is important that those around them do everything they can to help them retain their sense of identity and their feelings of worth. They will need to remember that:

- Each person with dementia is a unique individual with their own very different experiences of life, their own needs and feelings and their own likes and dislikes.
- Each person will be affected by their dementia in a different way.

Those caring for people with dementia will need to take account of their abilities, interests and preferences as they are at present, and the fact that these may change as the dementia progresses. They should be prepared to respond in a flexible and sensitive way.

Background information

The more background information you can give about the person's past, as well as their present situation, the easier it will be for others to see them as a whole person rather than simply as someone with dementia. They may then feel more confident about finding topics of conversation or suggesting activities that the person may enjoy.

You may need to remind others that:

- Dementia is nothing to be ashamed of and that it is no one's fault.
- Dementia may cause the person to behave in ways that others find irritating or upsetting but that this is not deliberate.

- People with dementia often remember the past far more clearly than the recent present and are often happy to talk about their memories, unless these are painful.

The right name

Our sense of who we are is closely connected to the name or names we are known by. It is important to make sure that others address the person with dementia in a way they recognise and prefer.

- Some people may be happy for anyone to call them by their first name or the name used by friends and family.
- Others may prefer younger people or those who do not know them well to use a courtesy title such as 'Mr' or 'Mrs'.

You may come from a cultural background which has its own particular way of using names and of addressing people in order to show respect. If so, make sure you explain this clearly to anyone from a different background who is in contact with the person with dementia so that they can use the appropriate name or courtesy title.

Culture and religion

Make sure that anyone caring for the person, however briefly, has appropriate details about any relevant cultural or religious customs or beliefs so that these can be respected. These may range from diet, clothing and the use of jewellery, for example, to ways of undressing, doing hair, washing or toileting. Some forms of touch which are taken for granted in some cultures may be thought disrespectful in others. You may need to explain any religious observances such as prayer and festivals as well as other traditions.

Treating as an adult

It is important that everyone continues to treat the person as an adult and with courtesy, however advanced their dementia.

- Be kind and reassuring without talking down to them as though they were a small child.
- Never talk over their heads as though they weren't there.

- Do not talk about the person in front of them unless they are included in the conversation.
- Avoid scolding or criticising the person as this will make them feel small.
- Look for the meaning behind what they may be trying to communicate, even if it does not seem on the surface to make sense.

Focus on abilities

Help the person avoid situations in which they are bound to fail since this can be humiliating. Look for tasks they can still manage and activities they can still enjoy.

- Give them plenty of praise and encouragement and let them do things at their own pace and in their own way.
- Do things with the person, rather than for them, so they can preserve some independence.
- Break activities down into small steps so that the person has some feeling of achievement, even if they can only manage part of a task.
- Much of our self-respect is often bound up in the way we look. Encourage the person to take a pride in their appearance and give them plenty of praise.

Respecting privacy

Try to make sure that the person's right to privacy is respected.

- You may suggest that people knock on their bedroom door before entering, for example.
- If the person needs help with intimate activities such as washing or going to the toilet this should be done in a sensitive way. Make sure the bathroom door is kept closed if other people are around.

Offering choice

It is important that the person with dementia should be informed and wherever possible consulted about matters which concern them. They should also be given every opportunity to make appropriate choices.

- Even if you are unsure how much they can understand, always explain what you are doing and why. You may then be able to judge their reaction from their expression or body language.
- Although too many choices can be confusing, you can continue to offer choice by phrasing questions that only need a yes or no answer such as, 'Would you like to wear your blue jumper today?'

Expressing feelings

People with dementia are likely to be sad or upset at times. They have the right to expect those caring for them to try and understand how they feel and to make time to offer support rather than ignoring them or jollying them along.

In the earlier stages people may want to talk about their anxieties and the problems they are experiencing. It is important that others do not brush these worries aside, however painful they may be, but listen and show that they are there for them.

Feeling valued

The person with dementia needs to feel respected and valued for who they are now, as well as for who they were in the past. It helps if those caring:

- are flexible and tolerant
- can make time to listen and to chat and enjoy being with the person
- can show affection as appropriate.

● The above information is from the Alzheimer's Disease Society. See page 41 for address details.

Fighting back

Some people with obsessive compulsive disorder (OCD) get better by themselves, but most people need help. Here is how we try to help young people with OCD

What is obsessive compulsive disorder?

Some young people have thoughts or ideas that keep coming into their minds even when they do not want them to. These thoughts often feel silly or unpleasant and are called obsessions. Compulsions are things people feel they have to do, even when they do not want to. Often people try to stop themselves from doing these things, but feel frustrated or worried unless they can finish. Problems with obsessions and compulsions can cause distress and worry, and can begin to affect young people at school, with their friends, and in their families. Many children have mild obsessions and compulsions at some time, but when it becomes a problem for the young person and their family, it is called obsessive compulsive disorder, sometimes called OCD for short.

Do many people have it and what causes it?

Recent studies show that OCD may affect as many as one in a hundred young people. We do not know the cause of OCD, but it usually has a lot to do with being anxious, and latest research suggests that a chemical imbalance in the brain may be involved. There is no suggestion that the way children are brought up causes OCD.

What can you do about it?

Some people with OCD get better on their own, but most need help. There are some treatments that are particularly useful, and these are the ones recommended by our clinic.

Assessment

Once the young person has been referred, we will write and offer an appointment if the type of difficulty seems appropriate for our clinic. Sometimes, with permission from the family, we will request information from the school and other professionals who have been involved.

The assessment in the clinic is tailored to the needs of the individual child or teenager, and will usually take 2-3 hours. We would ask parents to give a full account of the difficulties, and how they have dealt with the problem. The doctor will also perform a general physical examination.

Sometimes it is helpful to use tests, games or puzzles to look at abilities and difficulties in a variety of areas: reasoning, school work, etc. The clinic psychologist may be involved in this part of the assessment.

After the assessment we meet the family to feedback our findings, and to discuss what intervention would be helpful. We will also

---

Problems with obsessions and compulsions can cause distress and worry, and can begin to affect young people at school, with their friends, and in their families

---

feedback results of the assessment, and recommendations, to the referrer and the family doctor.

Treatment

Families may have come from a long distance to our clinic, or they may live locally. If the patient lives far away, sometimes it is most sensible for them to be referred back to local services for treatment. For children or teenagers who live near by, we may be able to offer treatment ourselves.

One of the first steps in treatment is helping young people and families understand obsessive compulsive disorder and how it affects them. Depending on the needs of the child and family, we might have family meetings to discuss this, and we may also see parents and the young person separately.

Medication

Medication can help some people with obsessive compulsive disorder. If drug treatment is considered appropriate, this will be discussed fully with the young person and family to help them decide whether they would like to try medication.

Behaviour therapy

Another helpful treatment for OCD is behaviour therapy. This involves a detailed assessment of the problem, often starting with the child and family keeping a diary of the obsessions and compulsions. The aim of the treatment is to teach young people how to get in control of the problem by tackling it a little bit at a time. Behaviour therapy needs to take place over several sessions. We may carry out some treatments ourselves or refer to local services with advice.

How well does the treatment work?

At least 70-80 per cent of children are likely to respond to treatment with medication and behaviour therapy. We would hope to offer the best treatments for OCD, many of which have been well tested in clinical trials and shown to be successful. Amongst the children we treat there will inevitably be some children we are unable to help. We would plan to inform families if this is the case so as not to continue with unhelpful treatment. Sometimes children have other difficulties in addition to OCD, such as developmental problems or depression, and these problems may need assessment and treatment if they do not change when the OCD improves.

• The above information is an extract from the King's College London and the South London and Maudsley NHS Trust web site which can be found at www.iop.kcl.ac.uk/main/MHP.htm

© Dr Isobel Heyman, Consultant Child & Adolescent Psychiatrist, Maudsley Hospital & Institute of Psychiatry, King's College, London.

The YoungMinds manifesto

Working to improve the mental health of children and young people

Children's mental health matters. When they have it they feel good about themselves, enjoy relationships, learn confidently and overcome their difficulties. When they don't – when they are over-whelmed by misery, anger or fear – all kinds of problems can arise.

Depression, eating disorders, behaviour problems, suicide attempts, drug and alcohol abuse, are all signs that children are having trouble getting on with their lives. These are children who are more likely to be excluded from school, to commit offences or to become homeless.

Recent government initiatives in relation to issues such as education, youth justice and child protection reflect an understanding of the pervasive influence of children's emotional experience.

But there are still serious challenges. There is a major gap between government policy and service delivery. Whilst strenuous efforts need to be made at all levels to reduce this gap, attention must simultaneously be paid to societal changes that are impacting on the mental health of children and young people in ways which are unclear. Changing family structures, shifts in patterns of employment and a commercialisation of childhood occurring against a background of rapid technological development have all played their part.

We know a good deal about the risk and protective factors for children's mental health and new developments, particularly in the fields of genetics and neuro-biology, are adding to our under-standing. To tackle these highly complex problems we need a national strategy, which integrates prevention, promotion and treat-ment approaches to support the mental health of children and young people. YoungMinds has outlined in this manifesto the areas which are our priorities as we move into the next millennium. We hope you will work with us.

In order to improve the mental health of children and young people we must make sure there will be:

1. Support for parents through a national transition to parent-hood programme

---

Depression, eating disorders, behaviour problems, suicide attempts, drug and alcohol abuse, are all signs that children are having trouble getting on with their lives

---

2. Help for schools to support children with mental health problems

3. Mental health services for young offenders and those at risk of offending

4. Comprehensive services to meet the needs of adolescents

5. Accessible, well co-ordinated emergency services for young people

6. Greater access to training for those who work with children and young people

7. Co-ordination across health, education and social services

8. The provision of well-staffed, specialist children's mental health services

9. Increased accountability for children's mental health services

10. An end to the postcode lottery of service provision

• The above is an extract from the YoungMinds Manifesto, if you would like a copy of the manifesto please send an A4 SAE to YoungMinds, 102-108 Clerkenwell Road, London EC1M 5SA.

ADDITIONAL RESOURCES

You might like to contact the following organisations for further information. Due to the increasing cost of postage, many organisations cannot respond to enquiries unless they receive a stamped, addressed envelope.

Alzheimer's Disease International
45-46 Lower Marsh
London, SE1 7RG
Tel: 020 7620 3011
E-mail: info@alz.co.uk
Web site: www.alz.co.uk
Works to improve the quality of life of people with dementia.

Alzheimer's Disease Society
Gordon House
10 Greencoat Place
London, SW1P 1PH
Tel: 020 7306 0606
Fax: 020 7306 0808
E-mail: info@alzheimers.org.uk
Web site: www.alzheimers.org.uk
Runs a helpline (0845 300 0336) offering advice and support for those affected by Alzheimer's disease.

Association for Postnatal Illness
25 Jerdan Place
Fulham, London, SW6 1BE
Tel: 020 7386 0868
E-mail: info@apni.org
Web site: www.apni.org
Works to increase public awareness of postnatal illness.

Depression Alliance
35 Westminster Bridge Road
London, SE1 7JB
Tel: 020 7633 0557
Fax: 020 7633 0559
E-mail: hq@depressionalliance.org
Web site: www.depressionalliance.org
Offers help to people with depression.

Manic Depression Fellowship Ltd
Castle Works, 21 St George's Road
London, SE1 6ES
Tel: 020 7793 2600
Fax: 020 7793 2639
E-mail: mds@mds.org.uk
Web site: www.mds.org.uk
Provides support and information for people with manic depression.

Mental Health Foundation (MHF)
20-21 Cornwall Terrace
London, NW1 4QL
Tel: 020 7535 7400
Fax: 020 7535 7474
E-mail: mhf@mentalhealth.org.uk
Web site: www.mentalhealth.org.uk

MHF is a UK charity improving the lives of everyone with mental health problems.

Mental Health Media (MHM)
The Resource Centre
356 Holloway Road
London, N7 6PA
Tel: 020 7700 8171
Fax: 020 7686 0959
E-mail: info@mhmedia.com
Web site: www.mhmedia.com
MHM works with the media and the fields of mental health and learning difficulties to challenge discrimination.

MIND
Granta House, 15-19 Broadway,
Stratford, London, E15 4BQ
Tel: 020 8519 2122
Fax: 020 8522 1725
E-mail: contact@mind.org.uk
Web site: www.mind.org.uk
MIND works for a better life for everyone experiencing mental distress.

National Schizophrenia Fellowship (NSF)
28 Castle Street
Kingston-upon-Thames, KT1 1SS
Tel: 020 8547 3937
Web site: www.nsf.org.uk
NSF is dedicated to improving the lives of everyone affected by severe mental illness.

Royal College of Psychiatrists
17 Belgrave Square
London, SW1X 8PG
Tel: 020 7235 2351
Fax: 020 7235 1935
E-mail: rcpsych@rcpsych.ac.uk
Web site: www.rcpsych.ac.uk
Produces an excellent series of free leaflets on various aspects of mental health.

SANE
1st Floor, Cityside House
40 Adler Street, London, E1 1EE
Tel: 020 7375 1002
Fax: 020 7375 2162
Raises awareness of serious mental illnesses. Saneline: 0345 67 8000

Schizophrenia Association of Great Britain (SAGB)
International Schizophrenia Centre
'Bryn Hyfryd', The Crescent
Bangor, Gwynedd, LL57 2AG
Tel: 01248 354048
Fax: 01248 354048
E-mail: sagb@btinternet.com
Web site: www.btinternet.com/~sagb
SAGB was the first association for schizophrenia in the UK.

Seasonal Affective Disorder Association (SADA)
PO Box 989
Steyning, Sussex, BN44 3HG
Tel: 01903 814942
Fax: 01903 879939
Web site: www.sada.org.uk
SADA informs the public and health professions about SAD and supports sufferers of the illness.

Threshold Women's Mental Health Initiative
14 St George's Place
Brighton, BN1 4GB
Tel: 01273 626444
Fax: 01273 626444
E-mail: thrwomen@globalnet.co.uk
Web site: www.users.globalnet.co.uk/~thrwomen
Threshold aims to identify the specific mental health needs of women. Runs the National InfoLine 0845 300 0911.

World Health Organisation (WHO)
20 Avenue Appia
1211-GENEVA 27, Switzerland
Tel: 00 41 22 791 2111
Fax: 00 41 22 791 3111
E-mail: info@who.ch
Web site: www.who.ch
WHO works to enhance both life expectancy and health expectancy.

YoungMinds
102-108 Clerkenwell Road
London, EC1M 5SA
Tel: 020 7336 8445
Fax: 020 7336 8446
E-mail: enquiries@youngminds.org.uk
www.youngminds.org.uk
Committed to improving the mental health of all young people.

INDEX

* * * * *

The Internet has been likened to shopping in a supermarket without aisles. The press of a button on a Web browser can bring up thousands of sites but working your way through them to find what you want can involve long and frustrating on-line searches.

And unfortunately many sites contain inaccurate, misleading or heavily biased information. Our researchers have therefore undertaken an extensive analysis to bring you a selection of quality Web site addresses.

Royal College of Psychiatrists
www.rcpsych.ac.uk
By clicking on <u>Press & Public</u> you can access information within their award-winning series of leaflets *Help is at Hand* or access their mental health factsheets including anxiety and phobias and schizophrenia.

Schizophrenia Association of Great Britain (SAGB)
www.btinternet.com/~sagb
Aims to offer help to everyone who needs information and support, as a sufferer, a relative friend of a sufferer, carer or medical worker.

YoungMinds
www.youngminds.org.uk
Click on <u>Info for Young People</u>. This takes you to useful information relating to young people and mental illness.

Mental Health Foundation
www.mentalhealth.org.uk
The Mental Health Foundation is the UK charity improving the lives of everyone with mental health problems or learning disabilities. By clicking on the <u>Information</u> section you can access information including 'Getting help if you have a mental health problem', 'Someone to Talk To: a list of organisations which can help' and 'Mental health problems and issues'. There is also a very extensive links page.

Depression Alliance
www.depressionalliance.org
Depression Alliance is a UK charity offering help to people with depression, run by sufferers themselves. This web site contains information about the symptoms of depression, treatments for depression, as well as Depression Alliance campaigns and local groups.

ACKNOWLEDGEMENTS

The publisher is grateful for permission to reproduce the following material.

While every care has been taken to trace and acknowledge copyright, the publisher tenders its apology for any accidental infringement or where copyright has proved untraceable. The publisher would be pleased to come to a suitable arrangement in any such case with the rightful owner.

Chapter One: What is Mental Illness?

Mental health, © World Health Organization (WHO), *Gender differences*, © 2000 Mental Health Foundation, *Serious mental illness*, © Royal College of Psychiatrists, *Victims of circumstance*, © Guardian Newspapers Limited, 2000, *Mental health – facts and figures*, © Crown copyright material is reproduced with the permission of the Controller of Her Majesty's Stationery Office, *Women and mental illness*, © Threshold Women and Mental Health Initiative, *The extent of mental health problems*, © Mental Health Foundation, *Phobias*, © David J. Hill BSc Hons (Psychol) 2000, *All about depression*, © 2000 Mental Health Foundation, *Older people and depression* © 2000 Mental Health Foundation, *Depression in children and young people*, © Royal College of Psychiatrists, *Postnatal depression*, © The Association for Postnatal Illness, *Seasonal affective disorder*, © Seasonal Affective Disorder Association (SADA), *All about dementia*, © 2000 Mental Health Foundation, *World prevalence of dementia*, © 2000 Mental Health Foundation, *Half of GPs ignore need for early diagnosis of dementia*, © Guardian Newspapers Limited, 2000, *Common questions about Alzheimer's Disease*, © Alzheimer's Disease Society, May 2000, *What is schizophrenia?*, © National Schizophrenia Fellowship (NSF), *Beginner's information about schizophrenia*, © Schizophrenia Association of Great Britain (SAGB), *Mental health and the media*, © Mental Health Media, *Key national findings*, © 2000 MIND, *Working on the verge of a breakdown*, © Guardian Newspapers Limited, 2000.

Chapter Two: Seeking Help

Depression, © Royal College of Psychiatrists, *Coping with depression*, © Depression Alliance, *Why did my world have to change?*, © Manic Depression Fellowship, *SANELINE*, © SANE, *Talking therapies*, © Robert Mond Memorial Trust (RMMT), *Understanding and respecting the person with dementia*, © Alzheimer's Disease Society, *Fighting back*, © King's College London and the South London and Maudsley NHS Trust, *The YoungMinds manifesto*, © YoungMinds.

Photographs and illustrations:

Pages 1, 8, 15, 26, 31, 36: Pumpkin House, pages 10, 17, 19, 28, 34, 39: Simon Kneebone.

Craig Donnellan
Cambridge
September, 2000